Junior Great Books

series 6

SECOND SEMESTER

◆ ◆ ◆

AN INTERPRETIVE READING, WRITING,

AND DISCUSSION CURRICULUM

JUNIOR GREAT BOOKS

SERIES 6   SECOND SEMESTER

THE GREAT BOOKS FOUNDATION

A nonprofit educational corporation

Published and distributed by

THE GREAT BOOKS FOUNDATION
A nonprofit educational corporation

35 East Wacker Drive, Suite 2300

Chicago, IL 60601-2298

CONTENTS

PREFACE   i

THE VELDT   1
Ray Bradbury

THE WHITE UMBRELLA   21
Gish Jen

THE PARSLEY GARDEN   33
William Saroyan

THE SECRET OF THE   43
YELLOW HOUSE
Anatoly Aleksin

AS THE NIGHT THE DAY   96
Abioseh Nicol

THE SUMMER BOOK   115
Tove Jansson

THE ALLIGATORS   134
John Updike

TWEEDLEDUM AND TWEEDLEDEE   144
(from THROUGH THE LOOKING-GLASS)
Lewis Carroll

THE MAGIC JACKET   160
Walter de la Mare

PROPS FOR FAITH   203
Ursula Hegi

LETTING IN THE JUNGLE   219
(from THE JUNGLE BOOKS)
Rudyard Kipling

THE SPRING RUNNING   256
(from THE JUNGLE BOOKS)
Rudyard Kipling

PREFACE

SHARED INQUIRY: A REVIEW

This is the beginning of your second semester of Junior Great
Books. You and the others in your class will again be reading
stories, writing questions about them, and discussing them.
As you know, Junior Great Books offers you an opportunity
to think for yourself about the meanings a story can have
and to build upon your ideas through *shared inquiry.* To take
an active part in shared inquiry you will be reading the stories
twice, making notes and thinking of questions as you read.
When your class discusses the story, you will need to listen
closely so that you can respond to the questions that your
teacher or leader asks and to the questions and ideas of your
classmates.

In shared inquiry, thoughtful readers come together to
interpret the meaning of a story. Leaders do not know the
answers to the interpretive questions they ask. They are not
waiting to hear one particular answer; they hope to discover
several good answers. A good answer is a logical one that can
be backed up with evidence from the story; any answer
you give is a good one if it helps to make sense of the story.
As you participate in shared inquiry, you will develop your
own interpretation of what you read. You will be working

to discover what the author wants to tell you or make you feel through his or her words.

Shared Inquiry Discussion is guided by these four rules:

1. **Only people who have read the story may take part in Shared Inquiry Discussion.**

2. **Discuss only the story everyone has read.**

3. **Do not use other people's opinions about the story unless you can back them up with evidence of your own.**

4. **Leaders may only ask questions; they may not answer them.**

INTERPRETIVE QUESTIONS

Some stories are simple and easy for us to understand. Others are more perplexing. In this second kind of story the author is trying to share with us ideas and feelings that are not obvious or easy to describe. You can fully understand such stories only if you actively seek their meaning out by asking questions.

As you read the stories in Junior Great Books, many questions will probably occur to you. Some of these questions will be factual, and in many cases a first reading of the story will answer them for you.

But other questions that occur to you will not be answered by the first reading. You may continue to wonder about these questions, and you may not find an answer that really satisfies you. You will need to look actively for the answers when you read the story again.

Questions that you cannot answer after the first reading are probably good interpretive questions. The second reading will help you bring these questions into focus and begin to look for possible answers to them.

In shared inquiry, you will need to read with a pencil in hand and to make notes as you read. While you are reading, mark the words and passages in the story that strike you as really important, interesting, or surprising. Mark places that make you think of a question. Mark parts that give you ideas about what the story means. Your teacher or leader may also ask you to watch for particular things during your reading and to give them special attention. Your notes will remind you of your thoughts while reading and help you to find evidence to back up what you say.

Remember that in shared inquiry there are three kinds of questions:

> **Questions of fact** ask you to recall particular details or events from a story. They have only one correct answer.

> **Questions of interpretation** ask you to think carefully about what happens in a story and to consider what the story means. Interpretive questions have more than one good answer that can be supported with what is said in the story.

> **Questions of evaluation** ask how the story fits with your own experience and, after you have interpreted it, whether or not you agree with what the story is saying.

Writing interpretive questions is one of the best ways to think on your own about the meaning of a story. Reading is not just a search for answers; it is also a search for new questions that you might want to raise. These are very often interpretive questions, some of which you may decide would be good to discuss. Here are some good sources of interpretive questions:

Words or passages that you think are important and that you wonder about

Parts of the story that you feel strongly about

Your curiosity about the characters

Your ideas about the story's meaning

ACTIVE LISTENING

When you think of discussing the stories in Junior Great Books, you probably think first of speaking—of answering the questions the leader asks. But most of the time you will be listening, not speaking.

Good listening is essential to good discussion. In shared inquiry, members of the group learn from one another by sharing questions, comparing notes, and exchanging ideas in response to questions. A response you hear from one of your classmates may prompt a new idea in you. By sharing this idea, you can prompt yet another idea in someone who is listening to you. As you listen to one another and explain your ideas to one another, the members of your group will discover new meanings in the story you have read. Discussion in Junior Great Books becomes like a conversation between friends who, because they listen closely to each other, can think thoughts together that they could not have thought alone.

Like good reading, good listening is active and responsive. When you exchange opinions with other members of your class you may feel surprise or excitement. You may strongly agree or disagree. And sometimes you will need to wait for a while to decide what you think. The first thing you notice as you listen may be whether the other person is agreeing with something you have said. But you will also want to understand *why* that person agrees or disagrees.

In shared inquiry, you have the opportunity to listen to the ideas of others and to respond. Like the leader, you may ask the others questions about what they have said. If you are not sure of what you think about a new idea that someone has put forward, asking questions is a good way to make things clearer. If you are sure, you can tell the person why you agree or disagree, backing up what you say with evidence from the text. Your questions and comments will help the group understand this participant better and lead everyone more deeply into the story.

Remember to look at your classmates when you are talking. This will help them pay close attention to what you say.

Good listening is a skill that takes time to learn. It isn't easy to follow everything that is said. It takes patience to listen to others and not to break in when they are trying to put their thoughts into words. When you are a good listener, you will not only be eager to discuss your own ideas. You will also be ready to respond thoughtfully to the ideas of others.

THE VELDT

Ray Bradbury

George, I wish you'd look at the nursery."

"What's wrong with it?"

"I don't know."

"Well, then."

"I just want you to look at it, is all, or call a psychologist in to look at it."

"What would a psychologist want with a nursery?"

"You know very well what he'd want." His wife paused in the middle of the kitchen and watched the stove busy humming to itself, making supper for four.

"It's just that the nursery is different now than it was."

"All right, let's have a look."

They walked down the hall of their soundproofed Happy-life Home, which had cost them thirty thousand dollars installed, this house which clothed and fed and rocked them to sleep and played and sang and was good to them. Their approach sensitized a switch somewhere and the nursery light flicked on when they came within ten feet of it. Similarly, behind them, in the halls, lights went on and off as they left them behind, with a soft automaticity.

"Well," said George Hadley.

They stood on the thatched floor of the nursery. It was forty feet across by forty feet long and thirty feet high; it had cost half again as much as the rest of the house. "But nothing's too good for our children," George had said.

The nursery was silent. It was empty as a jungle glade at hot high noon. The walls were blank and two-dimensional. Now, as George and Lydia Hadley stood in the center of the room, the walls began to purr and recede into crystalline distance, it seemed, and presently an African veldt appeared, in three dimensions; on all sides, in colors reproduced to the final pebble and bit of straw. The ceiling above them became a deep sky with a hot yellow sun.

George Hadley felt the perspiration start on his brow.

"Let's get out of the sun," he said. "This is a little too real. But I don't see anything wrong."

"Wait a moment, you'll see," said his wife.

Now the hidden odorophonics were beginning to blow a wind of odor at the two people in the middle of the baked veldtland. The hot straw smell of lion grass, the cool green smell of the hidden water hole, the great rusty smell of animals, the smell of dust like a red paprika in the hot air. And now the sounds: the thump of distant antelope feet on grassy sod, the papery rustling of vultures. A shadow passed through the sky. The shadow flickered on George Hadley's upturned, sweating face.

"Filthy creatures," he heard his wife say.

"The vultures."

"You see, there are the lions, far over, that way. Now they're on their way to the water hole. They've just been eating," said Lydia. "I don't know what."

"Some animal." George Hadley put his hand up to shield off the burning light from his squinted eyes. "A zebra or a baby giraffe, maybe."

"Are you sure?" His wife sounded peculiarly tense.

"No, it's a little late to be *sure*," he said, amused. "Nothing over there I can see but cleaned bone, and the vultures dropping for what's left."

"Did you hear that scream?" she asked.

"No."

"About a minute ago?"

"Sorry, no."

The lions were coming. And again George Hadley was filled with admiration for the mechanical genius who had conceived this room. A miracle of efficiency selling for an absurdly low price. Every home should have one. Oh, occasionally they frightened you with their clinical accuracy, they startled you, gave you a twinge, but most of the time what fun for everyone, not only your own son and daughter, but for yourself when you felt like a quick jaunt to a foreign land, a quick change of scenery. Well, here it was!

And here were the lions now, fifteen feet away, so real, so feverishly and startlingly real that you could feel the prickling fur on your hand, and your mouth was stuffed with the dusty upholstery smell of their heated pelts, and the yellow of them was in your eyes like the yellow of an exquisite French tapestry, the yellows of lions and summer grass, and the sound of matted lion lungs exhaling on the silent noontide, and the smell of meat from the panting, dripping mouths.

The lions stood looking at George and Lydia Hadley with terrible green-yellow eyes.

"Watch out!" screamed Lydia.

The lions came running at them.

Lydia bolted and ran. Instinctively, George sprang after her. Outside, in the hall, with the door slammed, he was laughing and she was crying and they both stood appalled at the other's reaction.

"George!"

"Lydia! Oh, my dear poor sweet Lydia!"

"They almost got us!"

"Walls, Lydia, remember; crystal walls, that's all they are. Oh, they look real, I must admit—Africa in your parlor— but it's all dimensional superactionary, supersensitive color film and mental tape film behind glass screens. It's all odorophonics and sonics, Lydia. Here's my handkerchief."

"I'm afraid." She came to him and put her body against him and cried steadily. "Did you see? Did you *feel*? It's too real."

"Now, Lydia . . ."

"You've got to tell Wendy and Peter not to read any more on Africa."

"Of course—of course." He patted her.

"Promise?"

"Sure."

"And lock the nursery for a few days until I get my nerves settled."

"You know how difficult Peter is about that. When I punished him a month ago by locking the nursery for even a few hours—the tantrum he threw! And Wendy too. They *live* for the nursery."

"It's got to be locked, that's all there is to it."

"All right." Reluctantly he locked the huge door. "You've been working too hard. You need a rest."

"I don't know—I don't know," she said, blowing her nose, sitting down in a chair that immediately began to rock and comfort her. "Maybe I don't have enough to do. Maybe I have time to think too much. Why don't we shut the whole house off for a few days and take a vacation?"

"You mean you want to fry my eggs for me?"

"Yes." She nodded.

"And darn my socks?"

"Yes." A frantic, watery-eyed nodding.

"And sweep the house?"

"Yes, yes—oh, yes!"

"But I thought that's why we bought this house, so we wouldn't have to do anything?"

"That's just it. I feel like I don't belong here. The house is wife and mother now and nursemaid. Can I compete with an African veldt? Can I give a bath and scrub the children as efficiently or quickly as the automatic scrub bath can? I cannot. And it isn't just me. It's you. You've been awfully nervous lately."

"I suppose I have been smoking too much."

"You look as if you don't know what to do with yourself in this house, either. You smoke a little more every morning and drink a little more every afternoon and need a little more sedative every night. You're beginning to feel unnecessary too."

"Am I?" He paused and tried to feel into himself to see what was really there.

"Oh, George!" She looked beyond him, at the nursery door. "Those lions can't get out of there, can they?"

He looked at the door and saw it tremble as if something had jumped against it from the other side.

"Of course not," he said.

At dinner they ate alone, for Wendy and Peter were at a special plastic carnival across town and had televised home to say they'd be late, to go ahead eating. So George Hadley, bemused, sat watching the dining room table produce warm dishes of food from its mechanical interior.

"We forgot the ketchup," he said.

"Sorry," said a small voice within the table, and ketchup appeared.

As for the nursery, thought George Hadley, it won't hurt for the children to be locked out of it awhile. Too much of anything isn't good for anyone. And it was clearly indicated that the children had been spending a little too much time on Africa. That *sun.* He could feel it on his neck, still, like a hot paw. And the *lions.* And the smell of blood. Remarkable how the nursery caught the telepathic emanations of the children's minds and created life to fill their every desire. The children thought lions, and there were lions. The children thought zebras, and there were zebras. Sun—sun. Giraffes—giraffes. Death and death.

That *last*. He chewed tastelessly on the meat that the table had cut for him. Death thoughts. They were awfully young, Wendy and Peter, for death thoughts. Or, no, you were never too young, really. Long before you knew what death was you were wishing it on someone else. When you were two years old you were shooting people with cap pistols.

But this—the long, hot African veldt—the awful death in the jaws of a lion. And repeated again and again.

"Where are you going?"

He didn't answer Lydia. Preoccupied, he let the lights glow softly on ahead of him, extinguish behind him as he padded to the nursery door. He listened against it. Far away, a lion roared.

He unlocked the door and opened it. Just before he stepped inside, he heard a faraway scream. And then another roar from the lions, which subsided quickly.

He stepped into Africa. How many times in the last year had he opened this door and found Wonderland, Alice, the Mock Turtle, or Aladdin and his Magical Lamp, or Jack Pumpkinhead of Oz, or Dr. Dolittle, or the cow jumping over a very real-appearing moon—all the delightful contraptions of a make-believe world. How often had he seen Pegasus flying in the sky ceiling, or seen fountains of red fireworks, or heard angel voices singing. But now, this yellow hot Africa, this bake oven with murder in the heat. Perhaps Lydia was right. Perhaps they needed a little vacation from the fantasy which was growing a bit too real for ten-year-old children. It was all right to exercise one's mind with gymnastic fantasies, but when the lively child mind settled on *one* pattern . . . ? It seemed that, at a distance, for the past month, he had heard lions roaring, and smelled their strong odor seeping as far away as his study door. But, being busy, he had paid it no attention.

George Hadley stood on the African grassland alone. The lions looked up from their feeding, watching him. The only flaw to the illusion was the open door through which he could see his wife, far down the dark hall, like a framed picture, eating her dinner abstractedly.

"Go away," he said to the lions.

They did not go.

He knew the principle of the room exactly. You sent out your thoughts. Whatever you thought would appear.

"Let's have Aladdin and his lamp," he snapped.

The veldtland remained; the lions remained.

"Come on, room! I demand Aladdin!" he said.

Nothing happened. The lions mumbled in their baked pelts.

"Aladdin!"

He went back to dinner. "The fool room's out of order," he said. "It won't respond."

"Or—"

"Or what?"

"Or it *can't* respond," said Lydia, "because the children have thought about Africa and lions and killing so many days that the room's in a rut."

"Could be."

"Or Peter's set it to remain that way."

"*Set* it?"

"He may have got into the machinery and fixed something."

"Peter doesn't know machinery."

"He's a wise one for ten. That I.Q. of his—"

"Nevertheless—"

"Hello, Mom. Hello, Dad."

The Hadleys turned. Wendy and Peter were coming in the front door, cheeks like peppermint candy, eyes like bright blue agate marbles, a smell of ozone on their jumpers from their trip in the helicopter.

"You're just in time for supper," said both parents.

"We're full of strawberry ice cream and hot dogs," said the children, holding hands. "But we'll sit and watch."

"Yes, come tell us about the nursery," said George Hadley.

The brother and sister blinked at him and then at each other. "Nursery?"

"All about Africa and everything," said the father with false joviality.

"I don't understand," said Peter.

"Your mother and I were just traveling through Africa with rod and reel; Tom Swift and his Electric Lion," said George Hadley.

"There's no Africa in the nursery," said Peter simply.

"Oh, come now, Peter. We know better."

"I don't remember any Africa," said Peter to Wendy. "Do you?"

"No."

"Run see and come tell."

She obeyed.

"Wendy, come back here!" said George Hadley, but she was gone. The house lights followed her like a flock of fireflies. Too late, he realized he had forgotten to lock the nursery door after his last inspection.

"Wendy'll look and come tell us," said Peter.

"She doesn't have to tell *me*. I've seen it."

"I'm sure you're mistaken, Father."

"I'm not, Peter. Come along now."

But Wendy was back. "It's not Africa," she said breathlessly.

"We'll see about this," said George Hadley, and they all walked down the hall together and opened the nursery door.

There was a green, lovely forest, a lovely river, a purple mountain, high voices singing, and Rima, lovely and mysterious, lurking in the trees with colorful flights of butterflies, like animated bouquets, lingering in her long hair. The African veldtland was gone. The lions were gone. Only Rima was here now, singing a song so beautiful that it brought tears to your eyes.

George Hadley looked in at the changed scene. "Go to bed," he said to the children.

They opened their mouths.

"You heard me," he said.

They went off to the air closet, where a wind sucked them like brown leaves up the flue to their slumber rooms.

George Hadley walked through the singing glade and picked up something that lay in the corner near where the lions had been. He walked slowly back to his wife.

"What is that?" she asked.

"An old wallet of mine," he said.

He showed it to her. The smell of hot grass was on it and the smell of a lion. There were drops of saliva on it, it had been chewed, and there were blood smears on both sides.

He closed the nursery door and locked it, tight.

In the middle of the night he was still awake and he knew his wife was awake. "Do you think Wendy changed it?" she said at last, in the dark room.

"Of course."

"Made it from a veldt into a forest and put Rima there instead of lions?"

"Yes."

"Why?"

"I don't know. But it's staying locked until I find out."

"How did your wallet get there?"

"I don't know anything," he said, "except that I'm beginning to be sorry we bought that room for the children. If children are neurotic at all, a room like that—"

"It's supposed to help them work off their neuroses in a healthful way."

"I'm starting to wonder." He stared at the ceiling.

"We've given the children everything they ever wanted. Is this our reward—secrecy, disobedience?"

"Who was it said, 'Children are carpets, they should be stepped on occasionally'! We've never lifted a hand. They're insufferable—let's admit it. They come and go when they like; they treat us as if *we* were offspring. They're spoiled and we're spoiled."

"They've been acting funny ever since you forbade them to take the rocket to New York a few months ago."

"They're not old enough to do that alone, I explained."

"Nevertheless, I've noticed they've been decidedly cool toward us since."

"I think I'll have David McClean come tomorrow morning to have a look at Africa."

"But it's not Africa now, it's Green Mansions country and Rima."

"I have a feeling it'll be Africa again before then."

A moment later they heard the screams.

Two screams. Two people screaming from downstairs. And then a roar of lions.

"Wendy and Peter aren't in their rooms," said his wife.

He lay in his bed with his beating heart. "No," he said. "They've broken into the nursery."

"Those screams—they sound familiar."

"Do they?"

"Yes, awfully."

And although their beds tried very hard, the two adults couldn't be rocked to sleep for another hour. A smell of cats was in the night air.

"Father?" said Peter.

"Yes."

Peter looked at his shoes. He never looked at his father anymore, nor at his mother. "You aren't going to lock up the nursery for good, are you?"

"That all depends."

"On what?" snapped Peter.

"On you and your sister. If you intersperse this Africa with a little variety—oh, Sweden perhaps, or Denmark or China—"

"I thought we were free to play as we wished."

"You are, within reasonable bounds."

"What's wrong with Africa, Father?"

"Oh, so now you admit you have been conjuring up Africa, do you?"

"I wouldn't want the nursery locked up," said Peter coldly. "Ever."

"Matter of fact, we're thinking of turning the whole house off for about a month. Live sort of a carefree one-for-all existence."

"That sounds dreadful! Would I have to tie my own shoes instead of letting the shoe tier do it? And brush my own teeth and comb my hair and give myself a bath?"

"It would be fun for a change, don't you think?"

"No, it would be horrid. I didn't like it when you took out the picture painter last month."

"That's because I wanted you to learn to paint all by yourself, Son."

"I don't want to do anything but look and listen and smell; what else *is* there to do?"

"All right, go play in Africa."

"Will you shut off the house sometime soon?"

"We're considering it."

"I don't think you'd better consider it anymore, Father."

"I won't have any threats from my son!"

"Very well." And Peter strolled off to the nursery.

"Am I on time?" said David McClean.

"Breakfast?" asked George Hadley.

"Thanks, had some. What's the trouble?"

"David, you're a psychologist."

"I should hope so."

"Well, then, have a look at our nursery. You saw it a year ago when you dropped by; did you notice anything peculiar about it then?"

"Can't say I did; the usual violences, a tendency toward a slight paranoia here or there, usual in children because they feel persecuted by parents constantly, but, oh, really nothing."

They walked down the hall. "I locked the nursery up," explained the father, "and the children broke back into it during the night. I let them stay so they could form the patterns for you to see."

There was a terrible screaming from the nursery.

"There it is," said George Hadley. "See what you make of it."

They walked in on the children without rapping.

The screams had faded. The lions were feeding.

"Run outside a moment, children," said George Hadley. "No, don't change the mental combination. Leave the walls as they are. Get!"

With the children gone, the two men stood studying the lions clustered at a distance, eating with great relish whatever it was they had caught.

"I wish I knew what it was," said George Hadley. "Sometimes I can almost see. Do you think if I brought high-powered binoculars here and—"

David McClean laughed dryly. "Hardly." He turned to study all four walls. "How long has this been going on?"

"A little over a month."

"It certainly doesn't *feel* good."

"I want facts, not feelings."

"My dear George, a psychologist never saw a fact in his life. He only hears about feelings; vague things. This doesn't feel good, I tell you. Trust my hunches and my instincts. I have a nose for something bad. This is very bad. My advice to you is to have the whole damn room torn down and your children brought to me every day during the next year for treatment."

"Is it that bad?"

"I'm afraid so. One of the original uses of these nurseries was so that we could study the patterns left on the walls by the child's mind, study at our leisure, and help the child. In this case, however, the room has become a channel toward—destructive thoughts, instead of a release away from them."

"Didn't you sense this before?"

"I sensed only that you had spoiled your children more than most. And now you're letting them down in some way. What way?"

"I wouldn't let them go to New York."

"What else?"

"I've taken a few machines from the house and threatened them, a month ago, with closing up the nursery unless they did their homework. I did close it for a few days to show I meant business."

"Ah, ha!"

"Does that mean anything?"

"Everything. Where before they had a Santa Claus now they have a Scrooge. Children prefer Santas. You've let this

15

room and this house replace you and your wife in your children's affections. This room is their mother and father, far more important in their lives than their real parents. And now you come along and want to shut it off. No wonder there's hatred here. You can feel it coming out of the sky. Feel that sun. George, you'll have to change your life. Like too many others, you've built it around creature comforts. Why, you'd starve tomorrow if something went wrong in your kitchen. You wouldn't know how to tap an egg. Nevertheless, turn everything off. Start new. It'll take time. But we'll make good children out of bad in a year, wait and see."

"But won't the shock be too much for the children, shutting the room up abruptly, for good?"

"I don't want them going any deeper into this, that's all."

The lions were finished with their red feast.

The lions were standing on the edge of the clearing watching the two men.

"Now *I'm* feeling persecuted," said McClean. "Let's get out of here. I never have cared for these damned rooms. Make me nervous."

"The lions look real, don't they?" said George Hadley. "I don't suppose there's any way—"

"What?"

"—that they could *become* real?"

"Not that I know."

"Some flaw in the machinery, a tampering or something?"

"No."

They went to the door.

"I don't imagine the room will like being turned off," said the father.

"Nothing ever likes to die—even a room."

"I wonder if it hates me for wanting to switch it off?"

"Paranoia is thick around here today," said David McClean. "You can follow it like a spoor. Hello." He bent and picked up a bloody scarf. "This yours?"

"No." George Hadley's face was rigid. "It belongs to Lydia."

They went to the fuse box together and threw the switch that killed the nursery.

The two children were in hysterics. They screamed and pranced and threw things. They yelled and sobbed and swore and jumped at the furniture.

"You can't do that to the nursery, you can't!"

"Now, children."

The children flung themselves onto a couch, weeping.

"George," said Lydia Hadley, "turn on the nursery, just for a few moments. You can't be so abrupt."

"No."

"You can't be so cruel."

"Lydia, it's off, and it stays off. And the whole damn house dies as of here and now. The more I see of the mess we've put ourselves in, the more it sickens me. We've been contemplating our mechanical, electronic navels for too long. My God, how we need a breath of honest air!"

And he marched about the house turning off the voice clocks, the stoves, the heaters, the shoe shiners, the shoe lacers, the body scrubbers and swabbers and massagers, and every other machine he could put his hand to.

The house was full of dead bodies, it seemed. It felt like a mechanical cemetery. So silent. None of the humming hidden energy of machines waiting to function at the tap of a button.

"Don't let them do it!" wailed Peter at the ceiling, as if he was talking to the house, the nursery. "Don't let Father kill everything." He turned to his father. "Oh, I hate you!"

"Insults won't get you anywhere."

"I wish you were dead!"

"We were, for a long while. Now we're going to really start living. Instead of being handled and massaged, we're going to *live*."

Wendy was still crying and Peter joined her again. "Just a moment, just one moment, just another moment of nursery," they wailed.

"Oh, George," said the wife, "it can't hurt."

"All right—all right, if they'll only just shut up. One minute, mind you, and then off forever."

"Daddy, Daddy, Daddy!" sang the children, smiling with wet faces.

"And then we're going on a vacation. David McClean is coming back in half an hour to help us move out and get to the airport. I'm going to dress. You turn the nursery on for a minute, Lydia, just a minute, mind you."

And the three of them went babbling off while he let himself be vacuumed upstairs through the air flue and set about dressing himself. A minute later Lydia appeared.

"I'll be glad when we get away," she sighed.

"Did you leave them in the nursery?"

"I wanted to dress too. Oh, that horrid Africa. What can they see in it?"

"Well, in five minutes we'll be on our way to Iowa. Lord, how did we ever get in this house? What prompted us to buy a nightmare?"

"Pride, money, foolishness."

"I think we'd better get downstairs before those kids get engrossed with those damned beasts again."

Just then they heard the children calling, "Daddy, Mommy, come quick—quick!"

They went downstairs in the air flue and ran down the hall. The children were nowhere in sight. "Wendy? Peter?"

They ran into the nursery. The veldtland was empty save for the lions waiting, looking at them. "Peter, Wendy?"

The door slammed.

"Wendy, Peter!"

George Hadley and his wife whirled and ran back to the door.

"Open the door!" cried George Hadley, trying the knob. "Why, they've locked it from the outside! Peter!" He beat at the door. "Open up!"

He heard Peter's voice outside, against the door.

"Don't let them switch off the nursery and the house," he was saying.

Mr. and Mrs. George Hadley beat at the door. "Now, don't be ridiculous, children. It's time to go. Mr. McClean'll be here in a minute and . . ."

And then they heard the sounds.

The lions on three sides of them, in the yellow veldt grass, padding through the dry straw, rumbling and roaring in their throats.

The lions.

Mr. Hadley looked at his wife and they turned and looked back at the beasts edging slowly forward, crouching, tails stiff.

Mr. and Mrs. Hadley screamed.

And suddenly they realized why those other screams had sounded familiar.

"Well, here I am," said David McClean in the nursery doorway. "Oh, hello." He stared at the two children seated in the center of the open glade eating a little picnic lunch. Beyond them was the water hole and the yellow veldtland; above was the hot sun. He began to perspire. "Where are your father and mother?"

The children looked up and smiled. "Oh, they'll be here directly."

"Good, we must get going." At a distance Mr. McClean saw the lions fighting and clawing and then quieting down to feed in silence under the shady trees.

He squinted at the lions with his hand up to his eyes.

Now the lions were done feeding. They moved to the water hole to drink.

A shadow flickered over Mr. McClean's hot face. Many shadows flickered. The vultures were dropping down the blazing sky.

"A cup of tea?" asked Wendy in the silence.

THE WHITE UMBRELLA

Gish Jen

When I was twelve, my mother went to work without telling me or my little sister.

"Not that we need the second income." The lilt of her accent drifted from the kitchen up to the top of the stairs, where Mona and I were listening.

"No," said my father, in a barely audible voice. "Not like the Lee family."

The Lees were the only other Chinese family in town. I remembered how sorry my parents had felt for Mrs. Lee when she started waitressing downtown the year before; and so when my mother began coming home late, I didn't say anything, and tried to keep Mona from saying anything either.

"But why shouldn't I?" she argued. "Lots of people's mothers work."

"Those are American people," I said.

"So what do you think we are? I can do the pledge of allegiance with my eyes closed."

Nevertheless, she tried to be discreet; and if my mother wasn't home by 5:30, we would start cooking by ourselves, to make sure dinner would be on time. Mona would wash the vegetables and put on the rice; I would chop.

For weeks we wondered what kind of work she was doing. I imagined that she was selling perfume, testing dessert recipes for the local newspaper. Or maybe she was working for the florist. Now that she had learned to drive, she might be delivering boxes of roses to people.

"I don't think so," said Mona as we walked to our piano lesson after school. "She would've hit something by now."

A gust of wind littered the street with leaves.

"Maybe we better hurry up," she went on, looking at the sky. "It's going to pour."

"But we're too early." Her lesson didn't begin until 4:00, mine until 4:30, so we usually tried to walk as slowly as we could. "And anyway, those aren't the kind of clouds that rain. Those are cumulus clouds."

We arrived out of breath and wet.

"Oh, you poor, poor dears," said old Miss Crosman. "Why don't you call me the next time it's like this out? If your mother won't drive you, I can come pick you up."

"No, that's okay," I answered. Mona wrung her hair out on Miss Crosman's rug. "We just couldn't get the roof of our car to close, is all. We took it to the beach last summer and got sand in the mechanism." I pronounced this last word carefully, as if the credibility of my lie depended on its middle syllable. "It's never been the same." I thought for a second. "It's a convertible."

"Well then make yourselves at home." She exchanged looks with Eugenie Roberts, whose lesson we were interrupting. Eugenie smiled good-naturedly. "The towels are in the closet across from the bathroom."

Huddling at the end of Miss Crosman's nine-foot leatherette couch, Mona and I watched Eugenie play. She was a grade ahead of me and, according to school rumor, had a boyfriend in high school. I believed it. Aside from her ballooning figure, she had auburn hair, blue eyes, and—I noted with a particular pang—a pure white folding umbrella.

"I can't see," whispered Mona.

"So clean your glasses."

"My glasses *are* clean. You're in the way."

I looked at her. "They look dirty to me."

"That's because *your* glasses are dirty."

Eugenie came bouncing to the end of her piece.

"Oh! Just stupendous!" Miss Crosman hugged her, then looked up as Eugenie's mother walked in. "Stupendous!" she said again. "Oh! Mrs. Roberts! Your daughter has a gift, a real gift. It's an honor to teach her."

Mrs. Roberts, radiant with pride, swept her daughter out of the room as if she were royalty, born to the piano bench. Watching the way Eugenie carried herself, I sat up, and concentrated so hard on sucking in my stomach that I did not realize until the Robertses were gone that Eugenie had left her umbrella. As Mona began to play, I jumped up and ran to the window, meaning to call to them—only to see their brake lights flash then fade at the stop sign at the corner. As if to allow them passage, the rain had let up; a quivering sun lit their way.

The umbrella glowed like a scepter on the blue carpet while Mona, slumping over the keyboard, managed to eke out a fair rendition of a catfight. At the end of the piece, Miss Crosman asked her to stand up.

"Stay right there," she said, then came back a minute later with a towel to cover the bench. "You must be cold," she continued. "Shall I call your mother and have her bring over some dry clothes?"

"No," answered Mona. "She won't come because she . . ."

"She's too busy," I broke in from the back of the room.

"I see." Miss Crosman sighed and shook her head a little. "Your glasses are filthy, honey," she said to Mona. "Shall I clean them for you?"

Sisterly embarrassment seized me. Why hadn't Mona wiped her lenses when I told her to? As she resumed abuse of the piano, I stared at the umbrella. I wanted to open it, twirl it around by its slender silver handle; I wanted to dangle it from my wrist on the way to school the way the other girls did. I wondered what Miss Crosman would say if I offered to bring it to Eugenie at school tomorrow. She would be impressed with my consideration for others; Eugenie would be pleased to have it back; and I would have possession of the umbrella for an entire night. I looked at it again, toying with the idea of asking for one for Christmas. I knew, however, how my mother would react.

"Things," she would say. "What's the matter with a raincoat? All you want is things, just like an American."

Sitting down for my lesson, I was careful to keep the towel under me and sit up straight.

"I'll bet you can't see a thing either," said Miss Crosman, reaching for my glasses. "And you can relax, you poor dear. This isn't a boot camp."

When Miss Crosman finally allowed me to start playing I played extra well, as well as I possibly could. See, I told her with my fingers. You don't have to feel sorry for me.

"That was wonderful," said Miss Crosman. "Oh! Just wonderful."

An entire constellation rose in my heart.

"And guess what," I announced proudly. "I have a surprise for you."

Then I played a second piece for her, a much more difficult one that she had not assigned.

"Oh! That was stupendous," she said without hugging me. "Stupendous! You are a genius, young lady. If your mother had started you younger, you'd be playing like Eugenie Roberts by now!"

I looked at the keyboard, wishing that I had still a third, even more difficult piece to play for her. I wanted to tell her that I was the school spelling bee champion, that I wasn't ticklish, that I could do karate.

"My mother is a concert pianist," I said.

She looked at me for a long moment, then finally, without saying anything, hugged me. I didn't say anything about bringing the umbrella to Eugenie at school.

The steps were dry when Mona and I sat down to wait for my mother.

"Do you want to wait inside?" Miss Crosman looked anxiously at the sky.

"No," I said. "Our mother will be here any minute."

"In a while," said Mona.

"Any minute," I said again, even though my mother had been at least twenty minutes late every week since she started working.

According to the church clock across the street we had been waiting twenty-five minutes when Miss Crosman came out again.

"Shall I give you ladies a ride home?"

"No," I said. "Our mother is coming any minute."

"Shall I at least give her a call and remind her you're here? Maybe she forgot about you."

"I don't think she *forgot*," said Mona.

"Shall I give her a call anyway? Just to be safe?"

"I bet she already left," I said. "How could she forget about us?"

Miss Crosman went in to call.

"There's no answer," she said, coming back out.

"See, she's on her way," I said.

"Are you sure you wouldn't like to come in?"

"No," said Mona.

"Yes," I said. I pointed at my sister. "She meant yes too. She meant no, she wouldn't like to go in."

Miss Crosman looked at her watch. "It's 5:30 now, ladies. My pot roast will be coming out in fifteen minutes. Maybe you'd like to come in and have some then?"

"My mother's almost here," I said. "She's on her way."

We watched and watched the street. I tried to imagine

what my mother was doing; I tried to imagine her writing messages in the sky, even though I knew she was afraid of planes. I watched as the branches of Miss Crosman's big willow tree started to sway; they had all been trimmed to exactly the same height off the ground, so that they looked beautiful, like hair in the wind.

It started to rain.

"Miss Crosman is coming out again," said Mona.

"Don't let her talk you into going inside," I whispered.

"Why not?"

"Because that would mean Mom isn't really coming any minute."

"But she isn't," said Mona. "She's *working*."

"Shhh! Miss Crosman is going to hear you."

"She's working! She's working! She's working!"

I put my hand over her mouth, but she licked it, and so I was wiping my hand on my wet dress when the front door opened.

"We're getting even *wetter*," said Mona right away. "Wetter and wetter."

"Shall we all go in?" Miss Crosman pulled Mona to her feet. "Before you young ladies catch pneumonia? You've been out here an hour already."

"We're *freezing*." Mona looked up at Miss Crosman. "Do you have any hot chocolate? We're going to catch *pneumonia*."

"I'm not going in," I said. "My mother's coming any minute."

"Come on," said Mona. "Use your *noggin*."

"Any minute."

"Come on, Mona," Miss Crosman opened the door. "Shall we get you inside first?"

"See you in the hospital," said Mona as she went in. "See you in the hospital with *pneumonia*."

I stared out into the empty street. The rain was pricking me all over; I was cold; I wanted to go inside. I wanted to be able to let myself go inside. If Miss Crosman came out again, I decided, I would go in.

She came out with a blanket and the white umbrella.

I could not believe that I was actually holding the umbrella, opening it. It sprang up by itself as if it were alive, as if that were what it wanted to do—as if it belonged in my hands, above my head. I stared up at the network of silver spokes, then spun the umbrella around and around and around. It was so clean and white that it seemed to glow, to illuminate everything around it.

"It's beautiful," I said.

Miss Crosman sat down next to me, on one end of the blanket. I moved the umbrella over so that it covered that too. I could feel the rain on my left shoulder and shivered. She put her arm around me.

"You poor, poor dear."

I knew that I was in store for another bolt of sympathy, and braced myself by staring up into the umbrella.

"You know, I very much wanted to have children when I was younger," she continued.

"You did?"

She stared at me a minute. Her face looked dry and crusty, like day-old frosting.

"I did. But then I never got married."

I twirled the umbrella around again.

"This is the most beautiful umbrella I have ever seen," I said. "Ever, in my whole life."

"Do you have an umbrella?"

"No. But my mother's going to get me one just like this for Christmas."

"Is she? I tell you what. You don't have to wait until Christmas. You can have this one."

"But this one belongs to Eugenie Roberts," I protested. "I have to give it back to her tomorrow in school."

"Who told you it belongs to Eugenie? It's not Eugenie's. It's mine. And now I'm giving it to you, so it's yours."

"It is?"

She hugged me tighter. "That's right. It's all yours."

"It's mine?" I didn't know what to say. "Mine?" Suddenly I was jumping up and down in the rain. "It's beautiful! Oh! It's beautiful!" I laughed.

Miss Crosman laughed too, even though she was getting all wet.

"Thank you, Miss Crosman. Thank you very much. Thanks a zillion. It's beautiful. It's *stupendous*!"

"You're quite welcome," she said.

"Thank you," I said again, but that didn't seem like enough. Suddenly I knew just what she wanted to hear. "I wish you were my mother."

Right away I felt bad.

"You shouldn't say that," she said, but her face was opening into a huge smile as the lights of my mother's car cautiously turned the corner. I quickly collapsed the umbrella and put it up my skirt, holding onto it from the outside, through the material.

"Mona!" I shouted into the house. "Mona! Hurry up! Mom's here! I told you she was coming!"

Then I ran away from Miss Crosman, down to the curb. Mona came tearing up to my side as my mother neared the house. We both backed up a few feet, so that in case she went onto the curb, she wouldn't run us over.

"But why didn't you go inside with Mona?" my mother asked on the way home. She had taken off her own coat to put over me, and had the heat on high.

"She wasn't using her noggin," said Mona, next to me in the back seat.

"I should call next time," said my mother. "I just don't like to say where I am."

That was when she finally told us that she was working as a check-out clerk in the A&P. She was supposed to be on the day shift, but the other employees were unreliable, and her boss had promised her a promotion if she would stay until the evening shift filled in.

For a moment no one said anything. Even Mona seemed to find the revelation disappointing.

"A promotion already!" she said, finally.

I listened to the windshield wipers.

"You're so quiet." My mother looked at me in the rear view mirror. "What's the matter?"

"I wish you would quit," I said after a moment.

She sighed. "The Chinese have a saying: one beam cannot hold the roof up."

"But Eugenie Roberts's father supports their family."

She sighed once more. "Eugenie Roberts's father is Eugenie Roberts's father," she said.

As we entered the downtown area, Mona started leaning hard against me every time the car turned right, trying to push me over. Remembering what I had said to Miss Crosman, I tried to maneuver the umbrella under my leg so she wouldn't feel it.

"What's under your skirt?" Mona wanted to know as we came to a traffic light. My mother, watching us in the rear view mirror again, rolled slowly to a stop.

"What's the matter?" she asked.

"There's something under her skirt?" said Mona, pulling at me. "Under her skirt?"

Meanwhile, a man crossing the street started to yell at us. "Who do you think you are, lady?" he said. "You're blocking the whole damn crosswalk."

We all froze. Other people walking by stopped to watch.

"Didn't you hear me?" he went on, starting to thump on the hood with his fist. "Don't you speak English?"

My mother began to back up, but the car behind us honked. Luckily, the light turned green right after that. She sighed in relief.

"What were you saying, Mona?" she asked.

We wouldn't have hit the car behind us that hard if he hadn't been moving too, but as it was our car bucked violently, throwing us all first back and then forward.

"Uh oh," said Mona when we stopped. "*Another* accident."

I was relieved to have attention diverted from the

umbrella. Then I noticed my mother's head, tilted back onto the seat. Her eyes were closed.

"Mom!" I screamed. "Mom! Wake up!"

She opened her eyes. "Please don't yell," she said. "Enough people are going to yell already."

"I thought you were dead," I said, starting to cry. "I thought you were dead."

She turned around, looked at me intently, then put her hand to my forehead.

"Sick," she confirmed. "Some kind of sick is giving you crazy ideas."

As the man from the car behind us started tapping on the window, I moved the umbrella away from my leg. Then Mona and my mother were getting out of the car. I got out after them; and while everyone else was inspecting the damage we'd done, I threw the umbrella down a sewer.

THE PARSLEY GARDEN

William Saroyan

One day in August Al Condraj was wandering through Woolworth's without a penny to spend when he saw a small hammer that was not a toy but a real hammer, and he was possessed with a longing to have it. He believed it was just what he needed by which to break the monotony and with which to make something. He had gathered some first-class nails from Foley's Packing House where the boxmakers worked and where they had carelessly dropped at least fifteen cents' worth. He had gladly gone to the trouble of gathering them together because it had seemed to him that a nail, as such, was not something to be wasted. He had the nails, perhaps a half pound of them, at least two hundred of them, in a paper bag in the apple box in which he kept his junk at home.

Now, with the ten-cent hammer he believed he could make something out of box wood and the nails, although he had no idea what. Some sort of a table perhaps, or a small bench.

At any rate he took the hammer and slipped it into the pocket of his overalls, but just as he did so a man took him firmly by the arm without a word and pushed him to the back of the store into a small office. Another man, an older one, was seated behind a desk in the office, working with papers. The younger man, the one who had captured him, was excited and his forehead was covered with sweat.

"Well," he said, "here's one more of them."

The man behind the desk got to his feet and looked Al Condraj up and down.

"What's *he* swiped?"

"A hammer." The young man looked at Al with hatred. "Hand it over," he said.

The boy brought the hammer out of his pocket and handed it to the young man, who said, "I ought to hit you over the head with it, that's what I ought to do."

He turned to the older man, the boss, the manager of the store, and he said, "What do you want me to do with him?"

"Leave him with me," the older man said.

The younger man stepped out of the office, and the older man sat down and went back to work. Al Condraj stood in the office fifteen minutes before the older man looked at him again.

"Well," he said.

Al didn't know what to say. The man wasn't looking at him, he was looking at the door.

Finally Al said, "I didn't mean to steal it. I just need it

and I haven't got any money."

"Just because you haven't got any money doesn't mean you've got a right to steal things," the man said. "Now, does it?"

"No, sir."

"Well, what am I going to do with you? Turn you over to the police?"

Al didn't say anything, but he certainly didn't want to be turned over to the police. He hated the man, but at the same time he realized somebody else could be a lot tougher than he was being.

"If I let you go, will you promise never to steal from this store again?"

"Yes, sir."

"All right," the man said. "Go out this way and don't come back to this store until you've got some money to spend."

He opened a door to the hall that led to the alley, and Al Condraj hurried down the hall and out into the alley.

The first thing he did when he was free was laugh, but he knew he had been humiliated, and he was deeply ashamed. It was not in his nature to take things that did not belong to him. He hated the young man who had caught him and he hated the manager of the store who had made him stand in silence in the office so long. He hadn't liked it at all when the young man had said he ought to hit him over the head with the hammer.

He should have had the courage to look him straight in the eye and say, "You and who else?"

Of course he *had* stolen the hammer and he had been caught, but it seemed to him he oughtn't to have been so humiliated.

After he had walked three blocks he decided he didn't want to go home just yet, so he turned around and started walking back to town. He almost believed he meant to go back and say something to the young man who had caught him. And then he wasn't sure he didn't mean to go back and steal the hammer again, and this time *not* get caught. As long as he had been made to feel like a thief anyway, the least he ought to get out of it was the hammer.

Outside the store he lost his nerve, though. He stood in the street, looking in, for at least ten minutes.

Then, crushed and confused and now bitterly ashamed of himself, first for having stolen something, then for having been caught, then for having been humiliated, then for not having guts enough to go back and do the job right, he began walking home again, his mind so troubled that he didn't greet his pal Pete Wawchek when they came face to face outside Graf's Hardware.

When he got home he was too ashamed to go inside and examine his junk, so he had a long drink of water from the faucet in the backyard. The faucet was used by his mother to water the stuff she planted every year: okra, bell peppers, tomatoes, cucumbers, onions, garlic, mint, eggplants, and parsley.

His mother called the whole business the parsley garden, and every night in the summer she would bring chairs out of the house and put them around the table she had had Ondro, the neighborhood handyman, make for her for fifteen cents, and she would sit at the table and enjoy the cool of the garden and the smell of the things she had planted and tended.

Sometimes she would even make a salad and moisten the flat old-country bread and slice some white cheese, and she and he would have supper in the parsley garden. After supper she would attach the water hose to the faucet and water her plants and the place would be cooler than ever and it would smell real good, real fresh and cool and green, all the different growing things making a green-garden smell out of themselves and the air and the water.

After the long drink of water he sat down where the parsley itself was growing and he pulled a handful of it out and slowly ate it. Then he went inside and told his mother what had happened. He even told her what he had *thought* of doing after he had been turned loose: to go back and steal the hammer again.

"I don't want you to steal," his mother said in broken English. "Here is ten cents. You go back to that man and you give him this money and you bring it home, that hammer."

"No," Al Condraj said. "I won't take your money for something I don't really need. I just thought I ought to have a hammer, so I could make something if I felt like it. I've got a lot of nails and some box wood, but I haven't got a hammer."

"Go buy it, that hammer," his mother said.

"No," Al said.

"All right," his mother said. "Shut up."

That's what she always said when she didn't know what else to say.

Al went out and sat on the steps. His humiliation was beginning to really hurt now. He decided to wander off along the railroad tracks to Foley's because he needed to think about it some more. At Foley's he watched Johnny Gale nailing boxes for ten minutes, but Johnny was too busy to notice him or talk to him, although one day at Sunday school, two or three years ago, Johnny had greeted him and said, "How's the boy?" Johnny worked with a boxmaker's hatchet and everybody in Fresno said he was the fastest boxmaker in town. He was the closest thing to a machine any packing house ever saw. Foley himself was proud of Johnny Gale.

Al Condraj finally set out for home because he didn't want to get in the way. He didn't want somebody working hard to notice that he was being watched and maybe say to him, "Go on, beat it." He didn't want Johnny Gale to do something like that. He didn't want to invite another humiliation.

On the way home he looked for money but all he found was the usual pieces of broken glass and rusty nails, the things that were always cutting his bare feet every summer.

When he got home his mother had made a salad and set the table, so he sat down to eat, but when he put the food in his mouth he just didn't care for it. He got up and went into the three-room house and got his apple box out of the corner of his room and went through his junk. It was all there, the same as yesterday.

He wandered off back to town and stood in front of the closed store, hating the young man who had caught him, and then he went along to the Hippodrome and looked at the display photographs from the two movies that were being shown that day.

Then he went along to the public library to have a look at all the books again, but he didn't like any of them, so he wandered around town some more, and then around half past eight he went home and went to bed.

His mother had already gone to bed because she had to be up at five to go to work at Inderrieden's, packing figs. Some days there would be work all day, some days there would be only half a day of it, but whatever his mother earned during the summer had to keep them the whole year.

He didn't sleep much that night because he couldn't get over what had happened, and he went over six or seven ways by which to adjust the matter. He went so far as to believe it would be necessary to kill the young man who had caught him. He also believed it would be necessary for him to steal systematically and successfully the rest of his life. It was a hot night and he couldn't sleep.

Finally, his mother got up and walked barefooted to the kitchen for a drink of water and on the way back she said to him softly, "Shut up."

When she got up at five in the morning he was out of the house, but that had happened many times before. He was a restless boy, and he kept moving all the time every summer. He was making mistakes and paying for them, and he had just tried stealing and had been caught at it and he was troubled. She fixed her breakfast, packed her lunch, and hurried off to work, hoping it would be a full day.

It was a full day, and then there was overtime, and although she had no more lunch she decided to work on for the extra money, anyway. Almost all the other packers were staying on, too, and her neighbor across the alley, Leeza Ahboot, who worked beside her, said, "Let us work until the work stops, then we'll go home and fix a supper between us and eat it in your parsley garden where it's so cool. It's a hot day and there's no sense not making an extra fifty or sixty cents."

When the two women reached the garden it was almost nine o'clock, but still daylight, and she saw her son nailing pieces of box wood together, making something with a hammer. It looked like a bench. He had already watered the garden and tidied up the rest of the yard, and the place seemed very nice, and her son seemed very serious and busy. She and Leeza went straight to work for their supper, picking bell peppers and tomatoes and cucumbers and a great deal of parsley for the salad.

Then Leeza went to her house for some bread which she had baked the night before, and some white cheese, and in a few minutes they were having supper together and talking pleasantly about the successful day they had had. After supper, they made Turkish coffee over an open fire in the yard. They drank the coffee and smoked a cigarette apiece, and told one another stories about their experiences in the old country and here in Fresno, and then they looked into their cups at the grounds to see if any good fortune was indicated, and there was: health and work and supper out of doors in the summer and enough money for the rest of the year.

Al Condraj worked and overheard some of the things they said, and then Leeza went home to go to bed, and his mother said, "Where you get it, that hammer, Al?"

"I got it at the store."

"How you get it? You steal it?"

Al Condraj finished the bench and sat on it. "No," he said. "I didn't steal it."

"How you get it?"

"I worked at the store for it," Al said.

"The store where you steal it yesterday?"

"Yes."

"Who give you job?"

"The boss."

"What you do?"

"I carried different stuff to the different counters."

"Well, that's good," the woman said. "How long you work for that little hammer?"

"I worked all day," Al said. "Mr. Clemmer gave me the hammer after I'd worked one hour, but I went right on working. The fellow who caught me yesterday showed me what to do, and we worked together. We didn't talk, but at the end of the day he took me to Mr. Clemmer's office and he told Mr. Clemmer that I'd worked hard all day and ought to be paid at least a dollar."

"That's good," the woman said.

"So Mr. Clemmer put a silver dollar on his desk for me, and then the fellow who caught me yesterday told him the

41

store needed a boy like me every day, for a dollar a day, and Mr. Clemmer said I could have the job."

"That's good," the woman said. "You can make it a little money for yourself."

"I left the dollar on Mr. Clemmer's desk," Al Condraj said, "and I told them both I didn't want the job."

"Why you say that?" the woman said. "Dollar a day for eleven-year-old boy good money. Why you not take job?"

"Because I hate the both of them," the boy said. "I would never work for people like that. I just looked at them and picked up my hammer and walked out. I came home and I made this bench."

"All right,'" his mother said. "Shut up."

His mother went inside and went to bed, but Al Condraj sat on the bench he had made and smelled the parsley garden and didn't feel humiliated anymore.

But nothing could stop him from hating the two men, even though he knew they hadn't done anything they shouldn't have done.

The Secret of the Yellow House

Anatoly Aleksin

My father and I are both named Sergei. If it hadn't been for this fact, nothing of this would ever have happened. I would not be on my way to the airline ticket office to hand in my plane ticket. I would not be giving up a trip I had dreamed of for so long.

It all began three and a half years ago, when I was still in the sixth grade.

1

"Your behavior is enough to refute every law of heredity," our zoology teacher would say to me. He was also our homeroom teacher. "It's impossible to imagine that you are your parents' son." He always found a direct relationship between people's behavior and their home life. Some of us came from happy homes, while others did not. But I among all the others came from a model family! That's exactly how our teacher put it: "You are a boy from a model family! How can you prompt another pupil during class?"

Perhaps it was his study of zoology that made him so aware of which of us belonged to which family.

I had been prompting my friend Anton. The kids all called him Cupcake, because he was plump and rosy-cheeked. Whenever he was embarrassed his round head would turn pink. It even seemed as though the roots of his blond hair became tinted pink by some inner glow.

Anton was unbelievably neat and conscientious, but whenever he was called on to recite he would be lost. Besides, he stuttered. The boys were always praying that the teacher would call on him, because Anton would take up a good half of the lesson. I would begin to fidget in my seat, mouth words, signal him with my hand—trying to prompt my friend in something he knew better than I did. This annoyed our teachers. It all ended with the two of us being put at the "emergency" desk. It was the first desk in the middle row, right next to the teacher's desk. According to our zoology teacher, only pupils who were a menace to the class were put at this desk.

Our homeroom teacher didn't bother to wonder about the source of Anton's difficulties. It was all as clear as day to him: Anton came from a broken home. His parents had separated ages ago, and he had never seen his father. Our zoology teacher was convinced that if Anton's parents had not gotten divorced, my friend would never feel shy or awkward when called on in class, and, perhaps, he would not stutter.

Things were much more complicated in my case, because I was refuting every law of heredity. My parents attended every parents' meeting, yet I was a poor speller. They always signed my report card on time, yet I often sneaked off from the last lesson. They coached a sports club at school, yet I prompted my friend Anton.

Hardly anyone at school knew the names of the pupils' parents. They were usually referred to as "Ivanov's parents," "Sidorov's parents," etc. My parents, however, were something apart. They were never judged by my behavior and actions, something that might have cast a shadow on their reputation as civic-minded parents and, as our zoology teacher put it, "true friends of the school."

This held true at home, as well. "What a happy family!" people would say of my parents, never blaming them for the fact that I had tried to reach a third-floor window with a stream of water from a hose the day before, though this is something other parents would never have been forgiven. "Truly, a model family," the neighbors, and especially the women, would say with a sigh. They seemed somehow to be reproaching someone as they watched Mother and Father out jogging every morning, rain or shine, or setting off to work and returning home again, arm in arm.

They say that people who have spent many years together come to resemble each other. My parents did. This was especially noticeable on a color enlargement which hung over the couch. Father and Mother, both tanned and dressed in light-blue gym suits, were looking into the camera. You'd think Charlie Chaplin had taken their picture from the way they were laughing. There were times when I thought it was a sound photograph, for I could actually hear their happy laughter. But Charlie Chaplin had nothing to do with it. My parents were simply very conscientious people. For instance, when there was a drive on for clearing up the yard and planting flowers and bushes, they'd be the first ones out on Sunday morning and the last to leave; if someone began a song during a festive occasion, they'd sing it right through, from the first to the last stanza, and not mumble half the words like so many others; and, if a photographer asked them to smile, just to smile, they would laugh as if they were watching a wonderful comedy.

Everything they did was extra good. No one was annoyed by this, because they did things in a very natural way. It seemed to be the only way they knew to do it. Even strangers could not visualize or speak of them separately. They always referred to my parents as "the Yemelyanovs." "The Yemelyanovs say . . ." "The Yemelyanovs believe . . ." "The Yemelyanovs are away on a business trip."

Mother and Father were often gone for weeks on end. They were both design engineers and would supervise the construction of new plants in other cities. On such occasions I remained at home with Grandma.

2

My parents resembled each other. I resembled Grandma, who was Mother's mother. This was more than an outward resemblance. Naturally, Grandma was happy for her daughter and proud of her son-in-law, my father; but, like me, she often made a shambles of the laws of heredity.

Father and Mother tried to harden us, to rid us once and for all of colds and infection (they never even had a sniffle, either one of them); but Grandma and I resisted. We didn't want to douse ourselves with icy water in the morning or get up earlier on Sundays than we did on weekdays just to go skiing or hiking. We were lax about our morning setting-up exercises. In fact, my parents often accused us of being lax. Lax about remembering to breathe properly when we did our exercises, lax about taking telephone messages for them, and informing them of the latest news dispatches, lax about keeping a strict schedule.

No sooner had we seen Mother and Father off on their latest business trip, than we'd hold a hurried council, just like a couple of plotters. Grandma, with her bobbed hair, small stature, and spare frame, was very much like a mischievous boy. And this boy was, as they say, the image of me.

"Well, now, how much are we laying aside for the movies?" Grandma would say.

"As much as possible!"

Then Grandma would lay aside as much as possible, because she enjoyed movies as much as I did. Next followed another important decision: We wouldn't bother cooking at home. Instead, we'd eat at the cafeteria that was on the ground floor of our house. I loved to eat at the cafeteria. We always saw eye to eye there.

"No use taking soup and a main dish," Grandma would sometimes say.

We often skipped the soup, and sometimes the main dish, too, but we always took pickled herring and two servings of fruit jelly. That was what we liked best. Besides, we were actually saving money for the movies!

If I was with Grandma I could get in to see films that had a "No children under 16" sign outside.

"I'm very frail," Grandma would say to the usher, turning old and decrepit before my eyes. "He accompanies me everywhere. I assure you he won't even look at the screen!"

"Pardon me for asking, but why are you looking at the screen?" she would say mischievously as we sat in the dark theater.

"I'm very frail," was a phrase that often got Grandma out of a tight spot.

"I'm very frail," she would say to escape from what my parents believed to be of the greatest value in prolonging her life, setting-up exercises and long, long walks.

We disliked doing the right things, Grandma and I, and this united us.

That year my parents had just left on a two months' trip. In unhappy families parents never write when they're away from home; in happy families they write once or twice a week. Grandma and I received a letter every single day. My parents took turns writing—one letter was from Mother, the next from Father, and so on. They never confused the order. Under the signature at the bottom of the page there was always a notation of the time, "8 A.M." That meant they did their letter-writting after their jogging and before leaving for work.

"It's fantastic!" Grandma exclaimed one day. "If they'd only confuse the order, just once!"

I couldn't understand from the way she said it whether she was delighted by my parents or was reproaching them. This was Grandma's distinctive quality—you could never tell whether she was joking or not, or whether she was praising something or making fun of it.

The next time she read the words "8 A.M." after Mother's signature, she said, "Well, I must say, your father is an excellent coach. My daughter is certainly in step with him now." Once again I wasn't sure whether she was praising Father, or whether this displeased her.

The mail deliveries were not as punctual as my parents. That is why the letters they wrote on schedule sometimes arrived in the morning and sometimes in the evening. More often in the morning, though. I'd open the mailbox and read the letter on my way to school. This was pleasant in many ways. First of all, I would begin my day by a sort of talk with Father and Mother, both of whom I missed very much. Then, if I happened to be late, I could wave the envelope at the teacher and say, "I just got a letter from my parents. It's very important. They're out of town!" And no one would say a word. I'd simply be told, "All right. Take your seat."

My parents never wrote much about themselves. Just, "We're very busy on the job, and we've been studying English in the evenings." They were learning it themselves, and would hold exams for each other from time to time. This astounded me. No one made them study, no one gave them marks for the work they did, but they crammed and

49

worried and wrote compositions! All by themselves; of their own free will. We usually admire people who do things we are not up to doing. And I admire my parents.

After a line or two about themselves, they'd devote the next three pages to valuable advice for Grandma and me. We hardly ever followed this advice, but we read and reread their letters with pleasure. They were thinking about us, and that always makes a person feel good.

Grandma and I preferred to reply by postcard. We bought the prettiest kind, and we felt that the photographs and paintings on them made up for the brief messages they carried. We'd always end by writing, "Letter follows," though none ever did.

One morning something unexpected happened. I opened the mailbox and found two letters there. Both had my name on them, "Sergei Yemelyanov." This had never happened before. I was used to getting a letter a day, but not two. That was going too far!

I opened the first envelope.

Sergei,

You must understand that if I have decided to write to you, it is because I simply must. I find myself in a very difficult situation. Even worse than on that memorable day in March . . . I have had a very bad shock, and you are the only person I can speak to, the only one I can (and want to) ask for advice. No one was ever closer to me than you, or ever will be. I know this to be true. I don't ask for your protection, for there is no one to protect me from. No one is to blame, everything turned out as it should have. Everything is quite normal, quite just. But there are times, you know, when everything is just and right, yet it does not make things easier for you. I'm usually back from work by six. I will be very grateful to you if you drop in any evening. If you can't drop by, I won't be offended. After all, you don't have to. You have the right not to wish to, as you did once before. This is quite natural and understandable. But I will be very grateful to you if you do drop in. Regards to your wife. I hope all is well.

There was no signature, just the initials "N.Y."

I usually read my letters on the run bumping into passersby and stumbling from time to time. Now I was standing stock-still on the stairway.

Who could have addressed Father by his first name, and have written so familiarly? There was a return address on the envelope, but it only had the same initials, "N.Y.," where the name should have been. Who was this woman? And why would there never be anyone closer to her than my father? Only Mother could have written such a letter to him!

But Mother had not written it.

I reread the letter. My hands were clammy. Then I found myself whispering the last line by heart, "Regards to your wife. I hope all is well." This calmed my fears a bit. "It must be a mutual acquaintance of theirs," I said to myself. "Sure, since she knows Mother. That's what she wrote, 'Regards to your wife.'"

Gradually, however, my voice took on a mocking tone, and the words seemed an insult to Mother.

"What are you mumbling about?" a neighbor asked, coming downstairs toward me.

Whenever I lied I usually did so in a loud, cheerful voice, so that no one would doubt the truth of what I was saying. This time, though, I said indifferently, "I'm studying my part for a play."

"It doesn't sound like a very happy part," the man said, passing me and continuing on down the stairs.

Then I remembered the second letter. It was Father's turn to write that day, and I suddenly wanted him to have written something very nice about Mother. But he hadn't, of course. Instead, his letter was full of various hopes. He hoped I would not forget to do my math homework; he hoped Grandma would not forget her age; he hoped we wouldn't be ordering pickled herring for dinner every day, because that had a very harmful effect on Grandma's system, and it was foolish to disregard this. As a true friend of the school he hoped that the sports club was functioning well in his absence. There wasn't a single word about Mother in his letter.

This seemed suspicious to me. And the very fact that Father always left for work with Mother and returned with her also began to seem suspicious now. It seemed to be done deliberately, just like my lies, when I tried to convince my elders I was telling the truth.

I was fifteen minutes late for class, but for some reason or other I didn't wave the envelope at the teacher. As luck would have it, our first class that day was zoology.

"They say, like father, like son," our zoology teacher said. "However, I see that this is not always the case. Far from it, in fact."

3

Up until that day life seemed so clear and simple that I rarely had any cause to stop and wonder about things. If I did find myself beset by doubts I never went to my parents, for their advice would be so obvious and sensible I could just as well have thought of it myself. It was easy to give this kind of advice, but very hard to follow it, because only model people like my parents could live up to it. I was not a model person and, therefore, I usually went to Grandma for advice. That day, however, I couldn't. After all, she was Mother's mother.

Sometimes I asked Anton for his advice. He would always listen to what I said attentively. The roots of his hair would turn pink, which meant he was trying to get at the bottom of my problem or question. Then he'd say, "I'll have to think about it. It's very serious."

Since there was really nothing serious about my problems, I usually forgot about them quickly, but my conscientious friend would take me aside in a day or two and say, "I've thought it over carefully."

"What?" I'd say carelessly.

Anton would begin to stutter terribly from a feeling of great responsibility in deciding a matter which I had already managed to forget about. This made me feel guilty, and I would listen to my friend with such grateful attention that the roots of his blond hair would seem to be on fire. Anton's advice rarely satisfied me. According to him, you always had to sacrifice yourself in the name of justice and truth. I, for one, didn't like to make sacrifices. But I trusted my best friend, and I knew that if real danger ever threatened me, I'd go to him and to no one else for help.

This danger had now materialized. I could not really say what it was as yet, but I could sense it. And that was probably the only kind of real trouble I could not tell my best friend about. Or anyone else, for that matter. How could I ever tell anyone that Father—my father!—was and would always be the closest person on earth to a woman I didn't even know? He wasn't even that close to Mother. I had heard her say, "There's no one closer to a mother than her child."

"That's a law of nature," Father had said. He always respects the law.

I could not tell Grandma or Anton about it, and so I decided to defend our home myself. At the same time, I would be defending my peace of mind and my carefree existence, which I now suddenly began to value. I, who had not yet accomplished anything, was going to defend the one thing that made me different from everyone else and that was such a source of pride to me—our model family.

The woman had written that she was usually at home by six. That was the time when I set out to see her. I had the address clearly written on the envelope. I took a bus for two stops, walked a short way, and stopped outside a small two-story yellow house. There was fancy stone carving over the windows. The cracks in the stone resembled the wrinkles on faces of old people. Old houses like that often have marble memorial plaques affixed to the outside. The shiny marble and glittering gold inscriptions look like new patches. They usually read, "So-and-so lived (or was born, or died) in this house." There was no marble plaque outside this house, though many people must have been born, and lived here, and died here.

I stood looking at the faded yellow house for a long time, suddenly too timid to enter. I didn't even know what I would say to the woman. I became unexpectedly interested in the house, looking at the cotton wool tucked between a set of double window frames to keep the cold out in winter. There was some confetti on it which had probably gotten stuck between the windows during a New Year's party. I looked at the icicles that hung over the windows. They were like bright crystal ornaments. What would I say to her? How would I begin?

Then I recalled the color poster that was tacked on the kitchen wall in a neighbor's apartment. She was an elderly, single woman. It showed a bathing beauty leaning on an oar, inviting everyone to "Take to the rivers in summer!" The elderly woman never took to the rivers, and I never knew why she had tacked the poster up in the first place. When Father saw it he said, "She's quite right. There's nothing more sensible than a vacation spent on the waterways." Father agreed with the lady on the poster, and this annoyed me. I compared her with Mother and became downhearted. The woman with the oar was also tanned, her teeth were also a flashing white, and her eyes were also merry, but she was prettier than Mother. That's why I belittled the bathing beauty. "I know people like her! They put on a bathing suit, but don't know how to swim. They pick up an oar, but don't know how to row. They walk around with a tennis racket, but never played tennis in their lives!"

As I walked up and down outside the old yellow house, not knowing what to do, I tried to imagine myself climbing the stairs and ringing the bell of apartment 7 (it was probably on the second floor). I'd hear unsuspecting steps. Then I'd assume a proud stance, hand her the letter, and say, "Did you write this?" "Yes," she'd reply softly. "I was asked to return it to you," I'd say, and leave.

But then I decided there was no use leaving so quickly. Perhaps we would have to battle it out. What if a beauty like the one on the neighbor's kitchen wall opened the door? What if she turned out to be more beautiful than Mother? Naturally, she was not as good a swimmer or skier as Mother. And she certainly wasn't as good an engineer. And no one admired her as people admired Mother. I'd tell her all about my mother, so that she'd forget all about trying to compete with her.

After I was properly worked up I dashed up the stairs. I was holding the letter in front of me. I probably looked like the neighbors did when we'd broken one of their windows while we were playing soccer. They'd come running to our parents, holding the ball right out in front of them, too, because it was evidence of our crime.

There was a nameplate outside the door. It read "N. Yemelyanova." N. Yemelyanova? What a strange coincidence. Maybe she was simply one of Father's relatives? Say a cousin, one I didn't know about. They'd simply forgotten to tell me about her. There was nothing strange about that. Maybe she had no parents, or no husband and children, and that made my father the person closest to her? That was very probable. Why, certainly! That was it!

My anger died away instantly. I suddenly became less sure of myself. I stuck the letter back into my pocket. Then I pulled it out again, remembering that the woman was in trouble. Strangely, I had not once thought of the lines that were probably the most important ones: "I find myself in a very difficult situation. Even worse than on that memorable day in March. I have had a very bad shock."

What had happened on that day in March? Perhaps someone had died. Or she had flunked an exam then, and someone had died now. Because she had written that things were even worse now. Why had I come then? I'd just tell her that Father was out of town. So that she wouldn't expect him.

I stuck the letter back into my pocket and rang the bell. I heard swift, impatient steps. Someone was practically running to the door; someone had been waiting for the bell to ring. But they hadn't been expecting me. A woman opened the door. It was rather dark on the landing.

"Whom do you want to see, child?" she asked after a while, as if she was trying to conceal her disappointment. It was strange to think that I had just heard her rushing toward the door, because she looked very tired.

"I'd like to speak to Yemelyanova."

"Have you come from Shurik?" she exclaimed. But she said it so softly she might have been speaking to herself. Then she repeated in a bare whisper, hopeful, yet afraid of being disappointed, "Have you come from Shurik?"

"No, I haven't."

4

When I entered the room I stopped dead in my tracks, for I saw my father.

I had never seen him looking like that before. He wasn't looking at me in his usual calm, confident, and happy way; his eyes looked confused, as if he was seeking help. And his hair was not combed back neatly as always. Here, his hair was disheveled, falling on his forehead and ears, which seemed unusually large, probably because his face was so thin and narrow. There were small dimples in his cheeks, something I had never noticed before.

His clothes were unrecognizable. He wasn't wearing his blue woolen shirt or a dazzling white shirt and a perfectly knotted tie, nor his fine suit with the white pinstripe. Here he had on a creased high-necked shirt, with the top buttons unbuttoned. The shirt was wrinkled because it was too big for Father's neck, which had never seemed so helplessly scrawny to me.

There was another photograph in which Father was in uniform. The soldier's tunic was also too big for him. He wore a fatigue cap with a star on his closely cropped head. He looked unhappy, even bitter.

"He sent me this one in 1941. He was at the front lines," the woman said unexpectedly. "It was a very difficult time."

She had a very calm and soothing voice, like the doctor and nurses when I had been in a hospital. They would say words like "serious" and "dangerous" in a way that told you they knew everything would be all right. These frightening words never sounded hopeless when they said them.

She could not understand why I just stood there, staring at the photographs on the wall. But she didn't say anything.

"That's my father," I finally said.

She came up close to me and gazed right into my face, the way very nearsighted people do. Somehow, you don't feel they are being rude or tactless.

This gave me a chance to get a closer look at her, too. She was very nearsighted. Her thick glasses in the heavy frames were apparently not strong enough, because she was squinting anyway. It was hard to guess her age. Her face was pale and tired-looking, but there was something about it that made her look young. Then I realized it was the heavy dark braid that was wound around her head like a crown.

Whenever Father would introduce me to one of his friends or colleagues, they'd always say, "He's a chip off the old block! He's the exact image of you," or something to that effect, although, actually, I resemble my mother's mother.

The woman kept looking at me, but she didn't say that I looked just like Father. She simply asked, "Did your father send you here?"

"My parents are away. They're out of town on business." I wanted to stress the fact that Father and Mother had gone together. But I found I couldn't say the word "mother" in her presence and so said "my parents."

"Will they be away for long?"

"About a year and a half," I lied, surprising myself. Then I added, "Or maybe two years. They don't know for sure." Then, in order to hide my embarrassment, I began to explain in detail. "Your letter was in the mailbox. When I took it out I thought it was from Father, but it was from you. I read it and thought . . ." I realized that one should never read other people's mail and stopped in midsentence. But only for a second. Then, because I was feeling still more embarrassed, I continued in still greater detail. "Father and I are both named Sergei. And it was still dark in the hall. I saw the name on the envelope and was sure it was for me. After I'd read most of it, I realized it wasn't. But then it was too late." I handed her the letter which I had already learned by heart. It was dog-eared from so much handling.

"So, you're Sergei, too? They named you after your father. That's understandable. You have a wonderful father. He's had such a difficult life. Especially in his youth. See how thin he is here. He was enrolled in a correspondence school and was working full time. Then he volunteered for front-line duty. I asked him not to, but he wouldn't hear of it. He was shell-shocked. I nursed him for such a long time."

"Are you a doctor?"

"Yes. He suffered terribly from insomnia. The one thing that could help him was sports, a rigid schedule, and the

60

will to keep to it. I had an awful time making him keep to it. Does he sleep well now?"

Father would often say that he slept like a log and never even dreamed. "What's the latest in dreams these days?" he'd say. "Technicolor or wide screen?" But I somehow couldn't bring myself to tell her this. "All right, I guess. So-so," I replied.

I was about to leave, yet she still hadn't said a word about my giving her regards to my father, or about asking him to come and see her when he returned.

"I don't know your name," I said as I stood in the doorway.

"Better late than never," she replied and smiled. "Although that's understandable. We were both a bit shy. My name is Nina Georgiyevna."

"She was Father's wife," I thought on the way home. "She didn't say so, but I'm sure of it. Here, in this little old yellow house, Father was thin and suffered from insomnia. And he studied. After work, in the evenings. And she must have helped him. He went off to the war from this house and returned here after the war. And she took care of him when he was so sick. But why didn't anyone ever tell me about it? Why? Not even Grandma, who shares a lot of secrets with me. Maybe Grandma doesn't know about it, either?"

At one of my parents' anniversary dinners Father had drunk to his first love. That meant Mother. Did that mean he had never loved this woman? Back home I asked Grandma, who was, as usual, reading something by Sir Walter Scott or Robert Louis Stevenson, whether a person's first love could come to him later in life. "Say, a man is married, but he hasn't met his first love yet. Does that ever happen?"

"You'll have to excuse me, but I've forgotten all about such things. Ask your father when he gets back."

"Why should I ask him?"

Grandma raised her head quickly from her favorite adventure story, something it was not easy to get her away from, and looked at me very solemnly, without her usual mischievous smile. Yes, she knew.

I looked at Father, laughing down on us from the photograph on the wall. There were no dimples in his cheeks, his neck was no longer helpless and scrawny. I suddenly didn't want to look at the photograph. But she herself had said that my father was a wonderful person. She herself had said it.

5

The next day I made a dash for the mailbox as soon as I was up, going out into the hall in my pajamas. I knew that there couldn't possibly be two letters for Sergei Yemelyanov in the box, but still, I had difficulty fitting the tiny mailbox key into the lock, something I had never had trouble doing before. There was a letter from Mother.

I didn't want to read it on my way to school as usual. I went into the bathroom, locked the door, and sat down on the edge of the tub. I studied each line intently, as I had never done before. Everything seemed to have a double meaning now. The first thing I noticed was that Mother's letter was very different from the ones that Father wrote. They must have always written differently, but I never noticed it. Now I did.

Father never wrote that he missed us and was in a hurry to get back, though I'm sure he missed us. He believed it was unwise to get himself, Grandma, and me upset for nothing since his trip was scheduled for a definite length of time and could not be shortened. Father often used words like "wise" and "unwise." "It's unwise to worry yourself and others," he would say.

Mother was a worrier. She wrote that she hoped I hadn't caught cold or gotten sick; she worried about Grandma's rheumatism. She promised that she'd never go away for so long again, but I knew that it wasn't up to her. I had overheard my parents talking before they had left. Father had said, "It's unwise not to want to check on the new plant. After all, it's our brainchild."

"He's our child, too," Mother had protested, pointing toward me. She hardly ever disagreed with Father, but when she did, it was timidly, as if she were surprised to find herself arguing with him.

Father reminded her of her duty as an engineer and said that since Grandma and I were both grown up, they could rely on us completely.

"He may be grown up, but I wouldn't say I was," Grandma said.

"Well, I'll say you both are. I know you'll never let us down," Father exclaimed.

If there was a difference of opinion, Father would often resort to grand-sounding phrases, which usually quickly decided things in his favor.

Mother wrote that she missed us both very much. She said she was making all sorts of plans for the time when she and Father would return. Nearly two whole pages were taken up with her plans. First, she and Father would finally teach me to get up at 6:30. Then the three of us would go jogging. Then, on Sundays, the four of us, Grandma included, would go to all the exhibits and museums. This was not the first time Mother had made such plans in her letters, and they had always seemed fine at a distance. I was ready to get up at the crack of dawn and race around the yard if only Mother and Father would come back home quickly. I was ready to go to exhibitions and museums (though Grandma and I preferred the movies) if only Mother and Father would come home soon.

This time, however, Mother's plans, and especially the part where she wrote, "Everything will be wonderful!" did not make me feel as happy as they usually did. A strange feeling that I couldn't understand kept me from feeling happy. It was as if I felt a bit embarrassed that everything would be "wonderful" again.

"That's silly," I said to myself, shaking off the uneasy feeling. "What nonsense! Father certainly would have graduated from college without her. And other doctors would have cured him just as well."

Grandma knocked on the bathroom door. I dashed off to dress with this last thought uppermost in my mind— Father certainly would have accomplished it all himself!

How could I ever have doubted it? After all, hadn't I seen him, even now, sitting up nights over his work, or studying English with no one there to make him study, but just so he could read all sorts of English technical journals?

I arrived at school feeling calm and quite contented with the world again. Anton got a C in physics, our last class that day. He knew the lesson but was too flustered to speak up.

"You'd be much better off having the teacher hear your recitation after the lessons are over, with just the two of you there. Then you'd never feel shy," I said, trying to cheer him up. "And don't go up in front of the class, just give her the answer from your seat. Want me to suggest it? I'll say it's because you stutter. You know why you always make out well in the written tests? That's because nobody's staring at you."

Since Anton always got A's and B's for his written work and made out so poorly when the teacher called on him, everyone was positive he was cribbing from me. It was terribly unfair, because it was me who always cribbed from him.

Anton was awfully upset that day. You could see it written all over his face. His face was round and plump, and you could read it like a book. I tried to cheer him up and said, "Let's go to the movies."

"I'm sorry, Sergei, but I can't. Mother's not on the night shift today, so she'll be home."

His mother is a telephone operator.

"We'll go with Grandma. If they won't let us in we'll say she's very frail and we're accompanying her. Understand?"

"I'm sorry, Sergei, I hate to say no, but when Mother's home . . ."

"You sit by her side and tell her stories, right?"

Anton was deep in thought. He didn't even answer me.

"I just don't know how I can show her my marks for today."

"Don't. Say you didn't get any."

"But I can't lie to her. She's had enough as it is."

"Enough of what?"

"She said, 'If nothing comes of you, either, I'll drown myself!' "

"What didn't come of who else?"

"Well, it's just that she thinks . . . that her life is ruined. I want to do something to make her . . . happy. But all I do is make her more unhappy. It's just the way everything seems to turn out."

Anton and I had been friends for over two years, but I'd never once been to his house. I imagine it wasn't a very happy house, and that was why he had never invited me over. I had never seen his mother, either. That day I imagined she must look like Nina Georgiyevna. And that made me think that I wanted to do something nice for Nina Georgiyevna, too. I hadn't even asked her what the bad shock she had had was. I didn't have the courage to. Or perhaps I had simply forgotten about it, because I was so interested in finding out as much as I could about my father. Although he was not in any trouble.

I didn't want Father to have to protect her, and so I had lied and said he was away for a year and a half. But certainly I could help her. Instead of him, that is.

Though I had returned her letter, I knew it by heart. As often happens, phrases from the letter would come back to me.

"If you can't drop by, I won't be offended. After all, you don't have to. You have the right not to wish to, as you did once before. . . ." I had not paid any attention to these words at first. Now I recalled them. Did that mean that she had written to Father once before, asking for his help, and that he had not replied? When had that been? And who was Shurik? Why was she so anxious to hear from him?

I was ready to protect her. But hadn't she written that there was no one to protect her from? Maybe she just wanted to speak to someone about her worries. It was more difficult to protect someone than to listen to what they had to say. On the other hand, you didn't need someone's permission to protect them, but if you wanted to share their worries they would first have to confide in you and tell you what they were.

Would Nina Georgiyevna confide in me? How could I know? I wasn't at all sure.

6

As I once again approached the little yellow house, I somehow forgot all about her worries. My one thought was to find out, as tactfully as possible, why she and Father had broken up. How should I go about asking her? Perhaps I'd say, "Why did Father stop living here?" No, that was all wrong. I couldn't even imagine Father living any place except with us. Or, "Why did you get divorced?" No, it was impossible to say these words out loud.

"Did you and Father fight?" I asked.

She smiled. "No, we didn't fight. It was something that just happened. I was much older than Sergei. It was understandable."

I suddenly felt grateful for the fact that Mother was seven years younger than Father. My happiness must have shown, because Nina Georgiyevna looked a bit surprised and adjusted her glasses. Then, in order to make up for my lack of tact, I said in an unnaturally loud and unnaturally concerned voice, "Are you in bad trouble?"

She obviously did not feel like answering a question like that, and so she did not. Instead, she went over to a photograph of a boy of three or four dressed in a sailor suit. The word "Viking" was printed in silver letters on the ribbon of his sailor hat. She began speaking, as if to herself. "After we separated I adopted a boy from a children's home. He was two and a half at the time. He was one of many children lost during the war. He's fifteen and seven months now."

She must have loved him very much if she knew his age to the month. That's how exact Mother would always be if she was speaking of my age. Father, on the other hand, always seemed to want to make me older. He'd say, "He's going on thirteen." Then I'd be cross with Mother for wanting to be exact. Since I was in such a rush to grow up at the time, I preferred Father's way of counting.

Nina Georgiyevna continued, "His parents turned up not long ago. This was to be expected. It was only natural."

She could not go on.

In order to break the silence I said softly, "Is his name Shurik?"

"How did you know?"

"You asked me if I'd come from Shurik when I came here yesterday. When you opened the door."

"Yes. He left with his parents. They're visiting relatives in the suburbs. He hasn't been back yet. I know their address, but I can't go there. Perhaps his parents want to give him a chance to get used to them. That's only natural. That's understandable." She sounded very tired. I could see how difficult this waiting was for her. She sat down on the couch. It was as if she was arguing with herself and I wasn't even there.

"When we separated many years ago, I felt wretched. But this is worse. When all is said and done, Shurik was my son. Now I must accept the fact that he is not mine. This is my second loss. I was younger then, and I had hopes for the future. Nothing remains to me now. The sentence of loneliness has been passed."

"Do you want me to go after him? To where he is now? And bring him back? Do you?"

She started, as if she was surprised that I had discovered her thoughts. "No. If people feel like coming over, they come of their own accord. They don't have to be brought. Don't you agree?"

I did, but I couldn't say so. What I said was, "You won't be alone now, Nina Georgiyevna. Would you like me to come and visit you? Every day, if you want me to. Honest! Do you?"

7

Sometimes, when wishing to comfort a person, we will promise the impossible. Or the nearly impossible.

"How can I visit her every day?" I wondered when I was back home again. "I can manage it now, but what about when my parents return?"

Whenever I was faced with a difficult problem I'd usually begin by convincing myself that it really wasn't important or even necessary for me to do whatever it was I had to do. I began by saying to myself, "Actually, I didn't promise her anything. I simply asked her whether she'd like me to visit her, and she didn't answer one way or the other. If she had really wanted me to visit her, she'd have said, 'By all means! I'll be so glad to see you!' But she didn't say a word. Now, how can I barge in on her without an invitation? Besides . . . when I said 'every day' that was, as our literature teacher says, 'a conscious exaggeration, a hyperbole.' She certainly realized it."

In short, I had soon convinced myself that there was no need to visit her every day.

All the same, I went to see her the very next day.

A boy of about fifteen opened the door. At the sight of him I straightened my fur hat which always sat lopsided on my head and, though I was now indoors, buttoned my coat up to my chin. The boy was neat and clean-looking. And handsome. He had wavy blond hair, blue eyes, and delicate pink cheeks.

He asked me politely and even kindly whom I wished to see. I usually felt at a loss and in awe of boys who were only two or three years older than I, much more so than of any adult. This was especially true of boys who were unlike me and who, I felt, were superior to me. I became so tongue-tied I nearly forgot Nina Georgiyevna's name for a moment.

"Come on in," the boy said.

He let me pass in front of him. I walked the length of the hall and knocked at the last door. He looked at me in surprise as I knocked, wondering how I knew the rooms in the house. But he didn't say anything. He opened the door hospitably . . . and I was looking at my father again. This made me stop in my tracks once again. The boy waited patiently. Finally, not knowing why I had stopped, he said, "Don't be shy. Go on in. She'll be back soon."

I felt that Nina Georgiyevna had taught him to be softspoken and polite. I entered and saw that the doors of both the bookcase and the closet were wide open. A suitcase stood open on the floor. As I passed into the room I glanced at it and saw a bright sweater and a couple of books in it.

"Take your coat off. And sit down on the couch. You can read one of the books here so you won't be bored waiting."

He pulled a heavy volume from one of the shelves without even reading the title and tossed it onto the couch. It was a medical book.

"Take your coat off, it's very warm in here," he repeated. It was thoughtful of him.

I looked at his neat suit and plaid shirt that was so well ironed it didn't have a single crease anywhere and recalled that I had gotten two fresh ink stains on my wrinkled school jacket that day. I decided not to take off my coat.

"Don't pay any attention to me. I'm packing." He proceeded to do just that.

The books on the shelves stood in even rows like soldiers on parade. As he pulled the volumes out, the rows became depleted, with empty spaces here and there. He would stop at times, and muse out loud, "I can't remember whether this is mine or not. I think it was a present from someone. If they had inscribed it, it would have made things easier." Once he stopped to say to me, "Clothes are easier. You can't get them mixed up." He was packing his shirts, shorts, and undershirts. He'd hold each item up to the light and run his hand over it, as if he was in a shop, deciding whether to buy it or not.

After I had caught my breath I decided it was stupid to sit there with my coat all buttoned up and play dumb. So I asked him a question to which I already knew the answer. "Are you Shurik?"

He turned to face me again. "How did you know? It's not written here," and he indicated his forehead. "This one says 'Viking.' " He pointed at the photograph of the boy in the sailor suit.

"I was here yesterday. Nina Georgiyevna told me. . . . She was waiting for you."

His face became stern, perhaps even a bit sad. "She loves me very much," he said with assurance. "And I love her very much, too, though she's a very strange person. Her head's in the clouds. She's very kind. Her kindness would have spoiled me if I hadn't put up a resistance. Believe me, it wasn't easy." He sighed, as if he was sorry for himself, because someone had been too kind to him. "There were times when we just couldn't see eye to eye. Now, when I've gotten to know my father, I realize it was my father's hard core that I had inherited that saved me."

He went on packing, then said, "I had to choose. A person can't have two mothers. Especially since my parents live in another city. That means I have to leave Nina Georgiyevna. And they love me very much, too. They searched for me for fifteen years. They never gave up hope. That means I have to disappear from this house and not leave any reminders behind. It'll be easier on Nina Georgiyevna that way. If you're going to dock a puppy's tail, you have to do it at one stroke. That's what my father said to me. He said there were kindhearted people who do it bit by bit, at a dozen strokes. They think that's more humane. That's why I didn't come to see her. I'm leaving now, but I'll write her a letter. I couldn't face saying goodbye to her."

I did not know why he was telling me all this.

He continued, "My parents are very grateful to Nina Georgiyevna. Although I would have been well taken care of at the children's home. Orphans are given the best of care in our country. Though you can't really compare it to having a home of your own. My parents wanted to write to her place of work and thank her officially, but she wouldn't even hear of it. Didn't I tell you her head was in the clouds?"

I decided he would never be accused of being "unwise." He was talkative, and all his sentences were measured and, somehow, too perfect. He was firmly convinced that Nina Georgiyevna loved him very much. He was firmly convinced that she might well have ruined him by her kindness, and that in our country orphans were well cared for. He was firmly convinced that his parents loved him very much, too, and that he had been sustained by his father's hard core that he had inherited. He never doubted that one lopped off a puppy's tail at a single stroke.

He kept referring to Nina Georgiyevna by name, though, as I suddenly realized, he had certainly called her "Mother" all these years. Not once had he made a slip, not once had he called her "Mother" now. And yet, at times I sensed something like a desire to explain or justify himself in his voice. That was probably why he had told me things I had not asked him about.

"Do you think I really need these shirts and books? My parents will get me new ones. I just don't want them to remind Nina Georgiyevna about me. It'll be hard enough on her as it is. It's better to disappear all at once, to go through it once and never think of it again. See what it says inside the top of my suitcase? 'Shurik Yemelyanov, Group 2.' This is the suitcase I took to summer camp when I was your age. She'll read the words over and over. What's the use of it? That's why I'm taking the suitcase, too."

I didn't like the idea of our both having the same last name. I had also noticed that he had scraggly blond sideburns that he had never yet shaved. They looked matted. This made his handsome face suddenly seem unpleasant to me.

He came up to me, put his hand on my shoulder, and said mysteriously, "What's your name?"

"Sergei."

"I want you to help me, Sergei. Wait here till Nina

Georgiyevna gets back. She should be home soon. Today's her day for parents. Tell her I was very upset, and that I said goodbye to her, even though she wasn't here. You have to wait for her anyway. You've come for consultation, haven't you?"

"What?"

"What do you mean—what? Aren't you one of her patients? Aren't you from my school?"

"No."

"Well! I was positive you'd come to consult her."

"About what?"

"She's the school doctor at my school. I mean, at my former school. And she holds extra consultation hours for parents and pupils at school, and even at home. That's a civic-minded person for you. It's fantastic. Half the time I could never relax at home. Some lout from school would barge in, strip to the waist, and start puffing like a locomotive, first through his nose, then through his mouth. Actually, something like that should be greatly respected. Except that no one has yet ever thanked her for all her trouble. At least I never heard them. But what did you come for?"

"It's about something else."

"Indeed? Well, we won't go into any details now. I've no time. Too bad you're not from my old school. I was about to do you a small favor. One good turn deserves another, as they say."

"What was it?"

"What's the use, if you're not from my old school? It was just a childish prank." He shrugged, as if embarrassed by the silliness of his childhood recollections. But he did go on, nonetheless. "She's as blind as a bat, you know. And very polite. Even if she doesn't believe you, she won't let you know it, so as not to embarrass you. 'Children are so vulnerable,' she would say. Naturally, none of the kids knew about this. Well, I tipped them off in a friendly way. I said that if they wanted to cut classes they could do so quite legally. I told them that if they sat about three feet away from her she wouldn't see a thing, and a fellow could tap on his thermometer and make it go up. It really made it look as though the kids had high fevers. Packs of kids would do it, especially before a test. It was as if an epidemic had hit the school. But she never noticed a thing. She'd write a slip for the teacher, excusing you from the lessons. It makes me laugh to even think about it! Well, those were the errors of youth. I wanted to do you a favor before I leave, to even up the score. Too bad you won't be able to make use of it."

He looked at his thin wristwatch solemnly. He noticed my eyes on him, and said offhandedly, "It's a present from my father." Then he began to hurry. "I'd better be going. Nina Georgiyevna will be home soon. I'd love to see her, but our meeting here would only pain her. It'll be better to write later on." He bent down to close the suitcase, but the lid wouldn't close. First, a shirttail got caught, then a pair of shorts. Finally, he sat on the lid and locked it. But a piece of his shorts still stuck out. He turned to me and said, "It's a good thing you're here. I'll write to her. You tell her I was very upset. It's a fact, you know. After all, I do love her. And I owe her a lot. But I'm not to blame if my real parents turned up."

8

"Now this one's left her, too," I said to myself when I heard the front door slam behind Shurik. However, he was back a moment later. I thought he had changed his mind and had decided to wait for her. Shurik put two keys on the table and said, "Give these to her, will you? This one's from the front door. Well, she knows which is which. It's bad luck to turn back once you've started out, though."

"I'm glad it is," I said to myself.

He was afraid to meet her on the way and set off at a trot, listing to one side, for the suitcase was very heavy. He was running away.

I looked at the little boy in the sailor suit. I like to compare old photographs with people I know, to see them, now grown-up or old and quite changed, as they once were.

"What a Viking you are! A regular knight in shining armor!" I said to myself. "To run off like that. So you think it'll be easier on her this way, do you? And life in the children's home would have been just as good, because orphans are well cared for in our country? Right. Everything is absolutely correct."

I tried to imagine Nina Georgiyevna buying Shurik his sailor suit many years ago. She had combed his hair carefully before the photographer had taken his picture. You could see a strand of the blond wavy hair lying nicely under the sailor hat. But she apparently hadn't gotten around to buying him a watch. Shurik and my father were side by side on the wall. It gave me an unpleasant feeling. "They're so different," I said to myself. "And they left this house under very different circumstances." I was certain of this, though I did not know exactly how my father had left. My memory, as if wishing to argue the point, kept bringing back snatches of Nina Georgiyevna's letter, the meaning of which I could not grasp: "If you can't drop by, I won't be offended. After all, you don't have to. You have the right not to wish to, as you did once before."

I heard the front door open and shut. Then I heard quick, light steps in the corridor. She was hurrying, she thought he might be waiting for her. Especially since, in his haste, Shurik had left the door open a crack and a strip of light from the room could be seen in the hall. I grabbed the keys from the table and stuck them in my pocket. I did it without thinking and only realized why I had done so later. The keys lying on the table were a sign of something final, of something lost and gone forever.

Nina Georgiyevna could not believe her eyes. She did not even say hello to me, but walked round the room. Then she said, "Is he hiding? He always liked to hide when he was little." She added in an undertone, "Is he in the wardrobe?" She opened the doors. Shurik's things had probably taken up all the space inside, because it was practically empty now.

Nina Georgiyevna sank down on a chair. We sat there, facing each other, our coats buttoned up to our necks.

"Was he here?"

I nodded.

"Where is he now?"

"He's gone. . . . He said he'll write to you."

She seemed to hunch over and lowered her head. I felt Shurik had struck her with his father's hard core that he had inherited. Her hat covered her dark braid, so that now there was nothing that made her look young. Her face was pale and wretched.

"Shurik will write to you," I said, trying to console her. "And you can write to him, too."

"He had to choose. And he chose his mother and father. That's only natural. It's understandable."

Something strange happened to me then. I couldn't just sit there any longer. Why was she always ready to "understand" those who caused her grief? Why did she believe that everything bad and unjust that happened to her was "only natural"? I didn't want to console her any more. I didn't speak, I practically shouted, "Your Shurik is a traitor! He betrayed you! He used what he knew about you against you. Just like a traitor!"

It was as if I had struck her.

She took off her glasses, as if she thought they were deceiving her, and it was not me who was shouting so loudly. I saw her eyes, so nearsighted, squinting and helpless. But I felt no pity. On the contrary, I wanted to get her all worked up, to see her indignant and as angry as I was, though I was not shouting as loudly now as before. Still, I persisted. "He told his friends that your eyesight was very poor. And that you were very kindhearted. They tricked you. They made the thermometers shoot up, so that they could cut classes. He was the one who told them how to fool you! And you believed them."

She lowered her head still more, and the look she gave me from under her brows was very strange. It was as if she was blaming me for what she had just heard. She wasn't blaming Shurik—oh, no!—she was blaming me!

I was upset by her reaction and tried to smooth things over. "That all happened long ago. When Shurik was still a little boy. He didn't know what he was doing. He was too young to realize it. But he's ashamed of himself now. He told me he was. Honest! Don't you believe me?" I was defending Shurik now, though she hadn't blamed him for anything. I was sort of apologizing for even daring to speak ill of him.

She wasn't listening to what I was saying. She was thinking out loud, "That's understandable. That's only natural. After all, I'm not a pediatrician, I'm a neurologist."

That meant she wasn't only blaming me, she was blaming herself, too. Everyone except Shurik. It was unbelievable. She continued, "That means I have no right to minister to children. I love them too much. Which again means I have no right. . . . So they tricked me, did they? That means they don't respect me."

"Oh, no! You're wrong! Only grownups don't try to fool a person they respect. But kids always do. Don't you believe me? Honest, we always do!"

She wasn't listening to me. I kept insisting, "I can tell you about any number of cases. For instance, we all respect our literature teacher very much. We even love her! The other day she said, 'Were you supposed to write a composition for today?' And we all hollered, 'No! You didn't give us any assignment!' Then she said, 'It must be sclerosis. I'm forgetting things.' Well, she doesn't have any sclerosis. We lied to her. We do it all the time. Don't you believe me? Honest, we do!"

I might as well have been talking to myself. My words did not penetrate. She continued thinking out loud, "He did it for his friends. That's understandable. But what about me? I have no right to be a school doctor. I love children, but apparently I don't know how to handle them. And that's what's so important. I'll have to think this over before the end of the school year. And decide."

What was I to do now? I had had no right to tell her about those thermometers!

She went over to the wall and took down Shurik's photograph. Then she pressed it to her heart and stroked the frame. And this, after what I had just told her.

9

My carefree life ended. I wasn't as happy-go-lucky as before. I felt that even my gait had changed, that I had slowed down, as if I had become heavier. Actually, I was still walking as quickly as ever, but my head had become heavier, because I was doing much more thinking than I ever had before. At times, I even blamed myself for things I had done, something that had never happened before.

I was upset the entire evening. Why had I told her about those thermometers? Did I think it would make her hate Shurik? Or was it because I couldn't stand her saying, "It's only natural" and "That's understandable"? But what if she decided to leave her post as the school doctor? She was just the kind of person who could do this. No, I could never let that happen! It was as if Father, having left that house, had entrusted Nina Georgiyevna to my care. Or, rather, had shifted the responsibility to me, and I could not free myself of it.

I kept comparing Father and Shurik in order to convince myself again and again that they had nothing in common. "Shurik betrayed her, but Father did not," I would say to myself. "Look at all the people in the world who get divorced. They're not to blame."

Be that as it may, Nina Georgiyevna now had no one in the world except me. And she didn't have me, either, because we hadn't yet become friends.

It's a known fact that when a truth, even an old truth, first strikes you, it seems like a revelation to you. That day I realized once and for all that a mother's love cannot be changed, no matter what. I had thought about this before. I had once read that parents love their sick or backward child more than they do their healthy, normal ones. I asked Grandma about it now.

"You're a case in point," she said. "Who else gets letters from their parents as often as you?" As usual, Grandma was joking. Naturally, there was nothing strange about the fact that my parents loved me. I was certain no one would ever wonder at that.

But what about Nina Georgiyevna? When I had told her about Shurik her eyes had been angry. Would she ever want to see me again? Still, I could not leave her all alone. I wondered what "alone" actually meant. When you're in trouble you can be surrounded by people, yet you'll still be all alone if these people are not your friends, or you do not need them. Did Nina Georgiyevna need me? Even if she didn't, I couldn't stay away and leave her all alone now. I'd have to think of something. There would be no problem if we were friends. You don't even have to be invited. You just go whenever you feel like it. But how could I go back after the conversation we had had?

I needed an excuse, and I started looking around for one. As a rule, I always found a way out of any difficult situation. "That's because you're a born dictator," Grandma once said. "You're convinced that the end justifies the means. It's always easier to do things that way—your hands are never tied."

Indeed, I could always lie, pretend, or play a trick if I had to. It was both easier and more fun to do things my way. However, my tricks were never very serious, nor were the goals that I pursued.

Now, for the first time in my life, I found myself in a difficult, unusual situation; but my mind, unwilling to consider it as such, rushed along the usual channels. I would have to find an excuse that would take me back to the little yellow house. At the same time, I wanted to prove to Nina Georgiyevna that she was a very good school doctor. Both these ideas would have to be combined. I would ask her help as a doctor, to cure a boy of a very dangerous illness. "It'd be better if it were fatal, and she saved him," I said to myself. But who would the boy be? Where would I find him? All of a sudden I realized that I was the likeliest person to be cured.

I quickly drew up a plan of action and put it into operation that very night. I was dying to sleep, but I made myself get up. Then I woke up Grandma, "I have a terrible case of insomnia, Grandma."

"What was that?"

"Oh, insomnia. It must be heredity."

"I'm too sleepy to understand you. What heredity?"

Then I recalled that Father had suffered from insomnia when he had lived in the yellow house, but Grandma might not know about it since he always slept like a log in our family. "Did Grandfather or Great-Grandfather suffer from insomnia?" I asked hopefully.

"As I recall, one of your two grandfathers was my husband, and he slept like a baby. I never knew your other grandfather, but to judge by your father . . ."

"Yes, that's right. He sleeps like a log. But I haven't been able to sleep for three nights in a row."

"Not even a wink?"

"Just a couple of winks."

"Hm. I see. It's a bit early for that, though."

"I know. Old people usually have insomnia."

"Watch what you say about old people, my boy. That's not what I meant. Are you in love? Why, as I recall, you were asking me about a person's first love a few days ago."

"I hope you don't think something like that would keep me awake! Ha! No, that's not it. I feel sick. And I want to go to a doctor. There's this doctor—she's a woman—who cures people of insomnia. I want to go to her."

"You've been on the go pretty much of late. I don't want to keep you cooped up, but freedom is supposed to produce progress, whereas it has only brought you poor marks in school."

"I don't have any poor marks."

"You will," Grandma said with confidence.

"If this insomnia keeps up, I might even be left back! But this doctor's a wizard. She cures people at her home. It's all absolutely free. All you have to do is write her a note. Just a few lines, where you'll say, 'I'm grateful to you for having saved my grandson,' or something like it. It'll please her no end."

"I can smell something fishy about this. But I'm very frail," Grandma said, becoming actually decrepit before my very eyes. "I'm very frail, and I have no strength to argue. Go to this doctor if you want to. Or to a professor. Or even to a hypnotist. Let them cure you, and get well. Just leave me alone and let me go back to sleep. I've taken two sleeping pills."

"Then maybe this awful heredity is from you!" I exclaimed happily.

"Don't be a nuisance."

Grandma, as usual, was willing to let me have my way. She was even willing to help me. Still, I sighed loudly for some time and tossed about. Then I got up twice to get a drink of water, making enough noise to be sure that she heard me.

After school the next day I decided to go and see Nina Georgiyevna as a patient. All the way to the bus stop I rehearsed what I would say to her. I always rehearsed a speech before trying to put something over. That was so I would have a ready answer for any unexpected questions.

This time, however, I was having real trouble rehearsing. The words that should have rolled off my tongue now sounded unconvincing and even silly. I took the part of Nina Georgiyevna in this imaginary conversation. Her words became harsher and angrier. Soon she was not at all like the Nina Georgiyevna I knew. Still, our conversation continued. I was listening to it as a third party, and one of the two people involved made me sick—namely, me.

"Are you getting on or not?" someone behind me said irritably. I was standing in front of the open bus door.

"No." I turned and slowly trudged homeward. I was at a loss. I could not understand what had happened. Why hadn't I been able to carry out the plan that had seemed so clever just a short while before?

Now, when so many years have passed, I realize that my childhood was ending, and in leaving me it was offering a kind of help that I could no longer accept.

10

I found that I could not deceive Nina Georgiyevna.

Still, I had to prove that I really believed in her as a doctor and that everyone else did, too. "At any cost!" I would have once said. But now any cost was out of the question. I was, as they say, restricted in my actions. It was more difficult to proceed under the circumstances.

How was I to achieve my goal without resorting to deception? Then I realized what an idiot I had been. Why had I gotten Grandma up in the middle of the night when I had Anton? A boy who really needed to be cured of shyness and stuttering! Besides, Nina Georgiyevna was a neurologist. She would cure my friend. Then we would write to thank her, and everyone in my class would sign it. She'd regain faith in herself. Everything about this plan was honest and aboveboard. After school that day I asked Anton to stay behind. "It's about a very serious matter," I said.

"Did anything happen?"

"Not yet. But it's going to very soon. I thought of a way to help your mother."

"What?"

I knew that Anton would never agree to my plan, and so decided to bring his mother into the scheme.

He was sitting at our "emergency" desk, while I sat at the teacher's desk. I decided my words would carry more weight that way. Anton was beginning to worry. I could see that by the way the roots of his hair were turning pink. I didn't want to keep him in suspense and so got right to the point.

"There's a woman doctor who's going to cure you. Beginning with tomorrow. She's an excellent neurologist. Understand? That's just what you need. Then you'll stop being shy, and your mother will be glad when she sees your report card."

"I'll have to think about it. It's a very serious thing."

"What's there to think about? I can't listen to you stuttering anymore! I don't want to watch you die every time the teacher calls on you!"

"Thanks, Sergei," Anton said, stuttering terribly from the impact of my unexpected proposal. "But that's the way I am. Doctors can't change that."

"Don't you remember what the zoology teacher said? Remember, he once said that your shyness was becoming morbid. And if it's unhealthy, that means it can be cured.

And she can cure you! Then the whole class will write her a letter to thank her."

"You mean all the kids will know about my going for treatment?"

"If you don't want them to, they won't. Just you and me. And your mother. Then the two of us will write to thank her."

"Do you have to write?"

"Sure. So that she'll have the letter as a remembrance."

"But Sergei . . . what if her medicine won't help me?"

"Please try to get cured. Can't you do such a little thing for my sake?"

"Do you really care about it that much? I never knew you did."

I was beginning to feel guilty, because I really hadn't been that sincere. As always, when I wanted to deceive someone, the words rolled smoothly off my tongue. I believe I wasn't acting very wisely again. "But Anton may really be cured!" I said to bolster up my courage. "That means everything is honest and aboveboard. The main thing is for Nina Georgiyevna to agree to it."

"I've come on very important business," I said as she opened the door. It sounded as if I was apologizing for having come.

She paid no attention to what I said. She didn't even ask what the important business was. "Have you come straight from school?"

"No, I stopped by at home first."

"Are you sure you're not hungry?"

"I ate at the cafeteria." And then I added, for no good reason, "Honest!"

"At a cafeteria?" she sounded surprised. "Are you all alone?"

"No, I live with Grandma."

"Is she your mother's mother?"

I nodded. We had never mentioned my mother before and we never mentioned her again. It was as if it was a forbidden subject. Never, not even once.

I recall that at that moment I wished that we would never again speak of my father, either. I would find out, this last time, something that was bothering me. It was a few lines in her letter that I could not understand. Then again, perhaps I did not want to hurry into the business that had brought me there.

"Nina Georgiyevna, you wrote that my father might not want to come to see you, 'as you did once before.'"

"Have you learned the letter by heart?"

"No. I just seem to have remembered those words. Did you ever write to him before?"

She was silent for some time, as if she could not decide whether or not to reply. Then she began to speak, as if she was thinking aloud. "What if Sergei had come then? Would things have turned out differently, as far as Shurik is concerned? Probably not. But I thought so at the time. Shurik was in the fourth grade then. I even remember the day. It was the twelfth of February. His classmates ganged up on him. I never pressed him for the reason. He was terribly offended, and he was dying to get even with them.

We were having supper. Right here, at this table. He told me all of his friends' secrets. Naturally, they were childish little secrets of very small boys. But he was convinced they were terrible secrets. That is why he spoke in a whisper and kept looking over his shoulder when he revealed them to me. He wanted me to tell the school principal about them so that the boys would be punished. I was the school doctor then, too, and was friendly with the principal. He died a while ago. Anyway, I refused. Shurik shouted and stormed and finally broke into tears. I was frightened. I couldn't seem to explain anything to him, I couldn't convince him he was wrong. That's when I decided he needed a man to talk to him. Not the principal or one of the teachers, but simply someone who was grown up and had a strong character. It had to be a man. I wrote to Sergei. There was no one else I could write to. I explained the situation to him. But he never replied. I suppose he was concerned about me. He was probably afraid seeing him again would upset me. That's understandable."

Naturally, Father had decided it was unwise to come. Or, perhaps, he felt it would be unfaithful to Mother and me. But was I being faithful to our family by coming here? This was a question I could not answer.

I looked at Father and Shurik side by side on the wall, so close I could touch them. Perhaps the same hard core Shurik had spoken about was part of Father, too? These thoughts were unpleasant, and I quickly banished them.

My next thought was pleasant. One could only share a secret about someone who was dear to one with a person who was also close, or, at least, with one you trusted. Did that mean that Nina Georgiyevna was beginning to trust me?

"Is that what you wanted to know? Was that your important business?"

"Oh, no!" I said quickly. "It's not that at all. My best friend, Anton, is badly in need of treatment. He needs to see a neurologist. He's terribly shy. He even stutters. All he gets are C's, even though he knows the lesson. He just stands there by the blackboard and doesn't say a word. Understand? He's afraid to say anything! And his mother says she'll drown herself if he doesn't eventually amount to anything. He's my best friend. If only you could cure him. That's what I came to see you about."

I had jumped up from my seat while I was speaking about Anton. She rose now and came very close to me, but not to see more clearly, as some nearsighted people do. I felt that she was standing so close to me so that I'd hear what she was saying, because she was practically speaking in a whisper.

I didn't know whether she had nodded toward Father or Shurik, because they were side by side on the wall, as she said, "In order to leave a person one sometimes has to invent a good reason. That's because the true reasons may be too cruel. But if one wants to come to a person, one doesn't have to invent anything. All one has to do is just come."

"Oh, but Anton is really very nervous! I want him to be cured. Don't you believe me? Honest, I do!"

"That goes without saying," she said softly. "We'll try to cure him."

That was three and a half years ago.

I have never told my parents that I know her. And she has never asked me whether I have said anything about her or not. Never, not even as a memory, did she enter our house. I was afraid to destroy something, I was afraid to hurt Mother. Mother was happy, and I treasured this happiness of hers. I was quite ready to do anything I could for Nina Georgiyevna. For Father, instead of Father.

Was it a call of duty? Yes, in the beginning, but not as time went on. "Call" is a fine word, and much more attractive than "compulsion," though their meanings are close. Perhaps the need to become someone's protector, someone's defender, came to me as the first call of manhood. You do not forget the first person who needed you.

Six months ago we moved to another city, to be closer to the factories my parents were designing. When I came to say goodbye to Nina Georgiyevna I promised her that I'd come to visit her each summer. In our desire to console people we sometimes promise them things that are later impossible to carry out. Or nearly impossible. I did not know my new address as yet, and we agreed that Nina Georgiyevna would write to me in care of General Delivery. That winter Father said I'd spend my summer holidays with Mother and him. We would go south, to the Black Sea coast.

"It's your last summer," Father said. "You'll be entering the university next autumn. You have to store up your energy and harden your muscles!"

"Your last summer." I was hearing these words spoken so often at home that I was beginning to feel I simply would not live to see another summer.

"Take to the rivers in summer!" the bathing beauty on the poster had been saying for so many years. Father had always said that she was absolutely right, that there was nothing more beneficial than a vacation spent boating. He was now trying to convince me that there was nothing more beneficial than mountain air, bathing in the sea, and sunning on the beach.

"We'll go by air," Father said. "I want you to enjoy your last summer."

I do like to enjoy myself. Besides, I had never flown before and had never been at the seashore. This last summer promised to be a memorable one, and I awaited its coming eagerly.

Last week Father bought our plane tickets. Today I received a letter in care of General Delivery. It read:

"I'm expecting you. I've taken a three months' vacation, to be free the whole summer. I decided not to accompany the children to summer camp. I'm waiting for you. However, if you find you cannot come, I will not be offended. I realize you might have other plans and things to do. This is quite understandable."

"I'll go to see her in January," I said to myself. "I'll have my winter vacation then."

I sat down to write a reply. I explained why it would be better for me to come next January, since I would not be able to go to the seashore in winter, and our northern city, where I had grown up, was so much better in winter than in summer, what with the skiing and all. I also said that she'd be better off going to summer camp as the camp doctor, because she'd be in the fresh air and would rest up, while it was dusty in the city in summer.

I reread my letter and felt I could not mail it. It was a stranger's letter, not something I had written. It was long and involved and there wasn't a single scratched-out word in it.

No. I would have to be at the little yellow house on the day I had promised to come, on the day she was expecting me. Or else I had no right to ever go there again.

I could not become her third loss. That is why I set out to turn in my plane ticket. I told my parents that I missed Grandma and Anton very much, for they had remained in the city of my childhood. I really do miss them. But I'm going there to visit Nina Georgiyevna. I won't send her a telegram with the time of my arrival on it. Instead, I'll open the door with the keys I still have. The ones that Shurik left on the table. She doesn't know I have them. The little yellow house should not only be witness to sad surprises.

Mother had not protested. She is glad that I'm so eager to go back and stay with Grandma.

I had an argument with Father today for the first time in my life. He said that my trip to our old home was foolish, that I should merely write to Grandma and Anton, that I could invite them to come and visit us later. He also said

I was upsetting our family plans, that I'd grown up lacking wings, since I was giving up the mountains, the heights, and our flight.

Still, I'm on my way to turn in my ticket.

Father quoted a passage from some book to me: "Man's life is a journey from the station of his birth to the station of his death with many steps and happenings on the way. One must traverse this route without getting detoured or falling behind schedule."

But I recalled that there are also planes and trains which travel on special routes and have no schedules. They are the most important ones, the rescue planes and trains. I did not say a word of this to Father. But I'm on my way to turn in my plane ticket now.

AS THE NIGHT THE DAY

Abioseh Nicol

Kojo and Bandele walked slowly across the hot green lawn, holding their science manuals with moist fingers. In the distance they could hear the junior school collecting in the hall of the main school building, for singing practice. Nearer, but still far enough, their classmates were strolling towards them. The two reached the science block and entered it. It was a low building set apart from the rest of the high school which sprawled on the hillside of the African savanna. The laboratory was a longish room and at one end they saw Basu, another boy, looking out of the window, his back turned to them. Mr. Abu, the ferocious laboratory attendant, was not about. The rows of multicoloured bottles looked inviting. A Bunsen burner soughed loudly in the heavy, weary heat. Where the tip of the light blue triangle of flame ended, a shimmering plastic transparency started. One could see the restless hot air moving in the minute tornado. The two African boys watched it, interestedly, holding hands.

"They say it is hotter inside the flame than on its surface," Kojo said, doubtfully. "I wonder how they know."

"I think you mean the opposite; let's try it ourselves," Bandele answered.

"How?"

"Let's take the temperature inside."

"All right, here is a thermometer. You do it."

"It says ninety degrees now. I shall take the temperature of the outer flame first, then you can take the inner yellow one."

Bandele held the thermometer gently forward to the flame and Kojo craned to see. The thin thread of quicksilver shot upward within the stem of the instrument with swift malevolence and there was a slight crack. The stem had broken. On the bench the small bulbous drops of mercury which had spilled from it shivered with glinting, playful malice and shuddered down to the cement floor, dashing themselves into a thousand shining pieces, some of which coalesced again and shook gaily as if with silent laughter.

"Oh my God!" whispered Kojo hoarsely.

"Shut up!" Bandele said, imperiously, in a low voice.

Bandele swept the few drops on the bench into his cupped hand and threw the blob of mercury down the sink. He swept those on the floor under an adjoining cupboard with his bare feet. Then, picking up the broken halves of the thermometer, he tiptoed to the waste bin and dropped them in. He tiptoed back to Kojo, who was standing petrified by the blackboard.

"See no evil, hear no evil, speak no evil," he whispered to Kojo.

It all took place in a few seconds. Then the rest of the class started pouring in, chattering and pushing each other. Basu, who had been at the end of the room with his back turned to them all the time, now turned round and limped laboriously across to join the class, his eyes screwed up as they always were.

The class ranged itself loosely in a semicircle around the demonstration platform. They were dressed in the school uniform of white shirt and khaki shorts. Their official age was around sixteen although, in fact, it ranged from Kojo's fifteen years to one or two boys of twenty-one.

Mr. Abu, the laboratory attendant, came in from the adjoining store and briskly cleaned the blackboard. He was a retired African sergeant from the Army Medical Corps and was feared by the boys. If he caught any of them in any petty thieving, he offered them the choice of a hard smack on the bottom or of being reported to the science masters. Most boys chose the former as they knew the matter would end there with no protracted interviews, moral recrimination, and an entry in the conduct book.

The science master stepped in and stood on his small platform. A tall, thin, dignified Negro, with greying hair and silver-rimmed spectacles badly fitting on his broad nose and always slipping down, making him look avuncular. "Vernier" was his nickname as he insisted on exact measurement and exact speech "as fine as a vernier scale," he would say, which measured, of course, things in thousandths of a millimetre. Vernier set the experiments for the day and demonstrated them, then retired behind the *Church Times* which he read seriously in between walking quickly down the aisles of lab benches, advising boys. It was a simple heat experiment to show that a dark surface gave out more heat by radiation than a bright surface.

During the class, Vernier was called away to the telephone and Abu was not about, having retired to the lavatory for a smoke. As soon as a posted sentinel announced that he was out of sight, minor pandemonium broke out. Some of the boys raided the store. The wealthier ones swiped rubber tubing to make catapults and to repair bicycles, and helped themselves to chemicals for developing photographic films. The poorer boys were in deadlier earnest and took only things of strict commercial interest which could be sold easily in the market. They emptied stuff into bottles in their pockets. Soda for making soap, magnesium sulphate for opening medicine, salt for cooking, liquid paraffin for women's hairdressing, and fine yellow iodoform powder much in demand for sprinkling on sores. Kojo protested mildly against all this. "Oh, shut up!" a few boys said. Sorie, a huge boy who always wore a fez indoors and who, rumour said, had already fathered a child, commanded respect and some leadership in the class. He was sipping his favourite mixture of diluted alcohol and bicarbonate—which he called "gin and fizz"—from a beaker. "Look here, Kojo, you are getting out of hand. What do you think our parents pay taxes and school fees for? For us to enjoy—or to buy a new car every year for

Simpson?" The other boys laughed. Simpson was the European headmaster, feared by the small boys, adored by the boys in the middle school, and liked, in a critical fashion, with reservations, by some of the senior boys and African masters. He had a passion for new motor cars, buying one yearly.

"Come to think of it," Sorie continued to Kojo, "you must take something yourself, then we'll know we are safe." "Yes, you must," the other boys insisted. Kojo gave in and, unwillingly, took a little nitrate for some gunpowder experiments which he was carrying out at home.

"Someone!" the lookout called.

The boys dispersed in a moment. Sorie swilled out his mouth at the sink with some water. Mr. Abu, the lab attendant, entered and observed the innocent collective expression of the class. He glared round suspiciously and sniffed the air. It was a physics experiment, but the place smelled chemical. However, Vernier came in then. After asking if anyone was in difficulties, and finding that no one could momentarily think up anything, he retired to his chair and settled down to an article on Christian reunion, adjusting his spectacles and thoughtfully sucking an empty tooth socket.

Towards the end of the period, the class collected around Vernier and gave in their results, which were then discussed. One of the more political boys asked Vernier: if dark surfaces gave out more heat, was that why they all had black faces in West Africa? A few boys giggled. Basu looked down and tapped his clubfoot embarrassedly on the floor. Vernier was used to questions of this sort from the senior boys. He never committed himself as he was getting near retirement and his pension, and became more guarded each year. He sometimes even feared that Simpson had spies among the boys.

"That may be so, although the opposite might be more convenient."

Everything in science had a loophole, the boys thought, and said so to Vernier.

"Ah! that is what is called research," he replied, enigmatically.

Sorie asked a question. Last time, they had been shown that an electric spark with hydrogen and oxygen atoms formed water. Why was not that method used to provide water in town at the height of the dry season when there was an acute water shortage?

"It is an impracticable idea," Vernier replied, shortly. He disliked Sorie, not because of his different religion, but because he thought that Sorie was a bad influence and also asked ridiculous questions.

Sorie persisted. There was plenty of water during the rainy season. It could be split by lightning to hydrogen and oxygen in October and the gases compressed and stored, then changed back to water in March during the shortage. There was a faint ripple of applause from Sorie's admirers.

"It is an impracticable idea," Vernier snapped.

The class dispersed and started walking back across the hot grass. Kojo and Bandele heaved sighs of relief and joined Sorie's crowd, which was always the largest.

"Science is a bit of a swindle," Sorie was saying. "I do not for a moment think that Vernier believes any of it himself," he continued. "Because, if he does, why is he always reading religious books?"

"Come back, all of you, come back!" Mr. Abu's stentorian voice rang out, across to them.

They wavered and stopped. Kojo kept walking on in a blind panic.

"Stop," Bandele hissed across. "You fool." He stopped, turned, and joined the returning crowd, closely followed by Bandele. Abu joined Vernier on the platform. The loose semicircle of boys faced them.

"Mr. Abu just found this in the waste bin," Vernier announced, grey with anger. He held up the two broken halves of the thermometer. "It must be due to someone from this class as the number of thermometers was checked before being put out."

A little wind gusted in through the window and blew the silence heavily this way and that.

"Who?"

No one answered. Vernier looked round and waited.

"Since no one has owned up, I am afraid I shall have to detain you for an hour after school as punishment," said Vernier.

There was a murmur of dismay and anger. An important soccer house-match was scheduled for that afternoon. Some boys put their hands up and said that they had to play in the match.

"I don't care," Vernier shouted. He felt, in any case, that too much time was devoted to games and not enough to work.

He left Mr. Abu in charge and went off to fetch his things from the main building.

"We shall play 'Bible and Key,' " Abu announced as soon as Vernier had left. Kojo had been afraid of this and new beads of perspiration sprang from his troubled brow. All the boys knew the details. It was a method of finding out a culprit by divination. A large door key was placed between the leaves of a Bible at the New Testament passage where Ananias and Sapphira were struck dead before the Apostles for lying, and the Bible suspended by two bits of string tied to both ends of the key. The combination was held up by someone and the names of all present were called out in turn. When that of the sinner was called, the Bible was expected to turn round and round violently and fall.

Now Abu asked for a Bible. Someone produced a copy. He opened the first page and then shook his head and handed it back. "This won't do," he said, "it's a Revised Version; only the genuine Word of God will give us the answer."

An Authorized King James Version was then produced and he was satisfied. Soon he had the contraption fixed up. He looked round the semicircle from Sorie at one end, through the others, to Bandele, Basu, and Kojo at the other, near the door.

"You seem to have an honest face," he said to Kojo. "Come and hold it." Kojo took the ends of the string gingerly with both hands, trembling slightly.

Abu moved over to the low window and stood at attention, his sharp profile outlined against the red hibiscus flowers, the green trees, and the molten sky. The boys watched anxiously. A black-bodied lizard scurried up a wall and started nodding its pink head with grave impartiality.

Abu fixed his aging bloodshot eyes on the suspended Bible. He spoke hoarsely and slowly:

> Oh, Bible, Bible, on a key,
> Kindly tell it unto me,
> By swinging slowly round and true,
> To whom this sinful act is due. . . .

He turned to the boys and barked out their names in a parade-ground voice, beginning with Sorie and working his way round, looking at the Bible after each name.

To Kojo, trembling and shivering as if ice-cold water had been thrown over him, it seemed as if he had lost all power and that some gigantic being stood behind him holding up his tired aching elbows. It seemed to him as if the key and Bible had taken on a life of their own, and he watched with fascination the whole combination moving slowly, jerkily, and rhythmically in short arcs as if it had acquired a heartbeat.

"Ayo Sogbenri, Sonnir Kargbo, Oji Ndebu." Abu was coming to the end now. "Tommy Longe, Ajayi Cole, Bandele Fagb . . ."

Kojo dropped the Bible. "I am tired," he said, in a small scream. "I am tired."

"Yes, he is," Abu agreed, "but we are almost finished; only Bandele and Basu are left."

"Pick up that book, Kojo, and hold it up again." Bandele's voice whipped through the air with cold fury. It sobered Kojo and he picked it up.

"Will you continue please with my name, Mr. Abu?" Bandele asked, turning to the window.

"Go back to your place quickly, Kojo," Abu said. "Vernier is coming. He might be vexed. He is a strongly religious man and so does not believe in the 'Bible and Key' ceremony."

Kojo slipped back with sick relief, just before Vernier entered.

In the distance the rest of the school were assembling for closing prayers. The class sat and stood around the blackboard and demonstration bench in attitudes of exasperation, resignation, and self-righteous indignation. Kojo's heart was beating so loudly that he was surprised no one else heard it.

> Once to every man and nation
> Comes the moment to decide . . .

The closing hymn floated across to them, interrupting the still afternoon.

Kojo got up. He felt now that he must speak the truth, or life would be intolerable ever afterwards. Bandele got up swiftly before him. In fact, several things seemed to happen all at the same time. The rest of the class stirred. Vernier looked up from a book review which he had started reading. A butterfly, with black and gold wings, flew in and sat on the edge of the blackboard, flapping its wings quietly and waiting too.

"Basu was here first before any of the class," Bandele said firmly.

Everyone turned to Basu, who cleared his throat.

"I was just going to say so myself, sir," Basu replied to Vernier's inquiring glance.

"Pity you had no thought of it before," Vernier said, dryly. "What were you doing here?"

"I missed the previous class, so I came straight to the lab and waited. I was over there by the window, trying to look at the blue sky. I did not break the thermometer, sir."

A few boys tittered. Some looked away. The others muttered. Basu's breath always smelt of onions, but although he could play no games, some boys liked him and were kind to him in a tolerant way.

"Well if you did not, someone did. We shall continue with the detention."

Vernier noticed Abu standing by. "You need not stay, Mr. Abu," he said to him. "I shall close up. In fact, come with me now and I shall let you out through the back gate."

He went out with Abu.

When he had left, Sorie turned to Basu and asked mildly: "You are sure you did not break it?"

"No, I didn't."

"He did it," someone shouted.

"But what about the 'Bible and Key'?" Basu protested. "It did not finish. Look at him." He pointed to Bandele.

"I was quite willing for it to go on," said Bandele. "You were the only one left."

Someone threw a book at Basu and said, "Confess!"

Basu backed onto a wall. "To God, I shall call the police if anyone strikes me," he cried fiercely.

"He thinks he can buy the police," a voice called.

"That proves it," someone shouted from the back.

"Yes, he must have done it," the others said, and they started throwing books at Basu. Sorie waved his arm for them to stop, but they did not. Books, corks, boxes of matches rained on Basu. He bent his head and shielded his face with his bent arm.

"I did not do it, I swear I did not do it. Stop it, you fellows," he moaned over and over again. A small cut had appeared on his temple and he was bleeding. Kojo sat quietly for a while. Then a curious hum started to pass through him, and his hands began to tremble, his armpits to feel curiously wetter. He turned round and picked up a book and flung it with desperate force at Basu, and then another. He felt somehow that there was an awful swelling of guilt which he could only shed by punishing himself through hurting someone. Anger and rage against everything different seized him, because if everything and everyone had been the same, somehow he felt nothing would have been wrong and they would all have been happy. He was carried away now by a torrent which swirled and pounded. He felt that somehow Basu was in the wrong, must be in the wrong, and if he hurt him hard enough he could convince the others and therefore himself that he had not broken the thermometer and that he had never done anything wrong. He groped for something bulky enough to throw, and picked up the Bible.

"Stop it," Vernier shouted through the open doorway. "Stop it, you hooligans, you beasts."

They all became quiet and shamefacedly put down what they were going to throw. Basu was crying quietly and hopelessly, his thin body shaking.

"Go home, all of you, go home. I am ashamed of you."
His black face shone with anger. "You are an utter disgrace
to your nation and to your race."

They crept away, quietly, uneasily, avoiding each other's
eyes, like people caught in a secret passion.

Vernier went to the first-aid cupboard and started
dressing Basu's wounds.

Kojo and Bandele came back and hid behind the door,
listening. Bandele insisted that they should.

Vernier put Basu's bandaged head against his waistcoat
and dried the boy's tears with his handkerchief, gently
patting his shaking shoulders.

"It wouldn't have been so bad if I had done it, sir," he
mumbled, snuggling his head against Vernier, "but I did
not do it. I swear to God I did not."

"Hush, hush," said Vernier comfortingly.

"Now they will hate me even more," he moaned.

"Hush, hush."

"I don't mind the wounds so much, they will heal."

"Hush, hush."

"They've missed the football match and now they will
never talk to me again, oh-ee, oh-ee, why have I been so
punished?"

"As you grow older," Vernier advised, "you must learn
that men are punished not always for what they do, but
often for what people think they will do, or for what they
are. Remember that and you will find it easier to forgive
them. 'To thine own self be true!' " Vernier ended with a
flourish, holding up his clenched fists in a mock dramatic
gesture, quoting from the Shakespeare examination set-

book for the year and declaiming to the dripping taps and empty benches and still afternoon, to make Basu laugh.

Basu dried his eyes and smiled wanly and replied: " 'And it shall follow as the night the day.' *Hamlet,* Act One, Scene Three, Polonius to Laertes."

"There's a good chap. First Class Grade One. I shall give you a lift home."

Kojo and Bandele walked down the red laterite road together, Kojo dispiritedly kicking stones into the gutter.

"The fuss they made over a silly old thermometer," Bandele began.

"I don't know, old man, I don't know," Kojo said impatiently.

They had both been shaken by the scene in the empty lab. A thin invisible wall of hostility and mistrust was slowly rising between them.

"Basu did not do it, of course," Bandele said.

Kojo stopped dead in his tracks. "Of course he did not do it," he shouted; "we did it."

"No need to shout, old man. After all, it was your idea."

"It wasn't," Kojo said furiously. "You suggested we try it."

"Well, you started the argument. Don't be childish." They tramped on silently, raising small clouds of dust with their bare feet.

"I should not take it too much to heart," Bandele continued. "That chap Basu's father hoards foodstuff like rice and palm oil until there is a shortage and then sells them at high prices. The police are watching him."

"What has that got to do with it?" Kojo asked.

"Don't you see, Basu might quite easily have broken that thermometer. I bet he has done things before that we have all been punished for." Bandele was emphatic.

They walked on steadily down the main road of the town, past the Syrian and Lebanese shops crammed with knickknacks and rolls of cloth, past a large Indian shop with dull red carpets and brass trays displayed in its windows, carefully stepping aside in the narrow road as the British officials sped by in cars to their hill-station bungalows for lunch and siesta.

Kojo reached home at last. He washed his feet and ate his main meal for the day. He sat about heavily and restlessly for some hours. Night soon fell with its usual swiftness, at six, and he finished his homework early and went to bed.

Lying in bed he rehearsed again what he was determined to do the next day. He would go up to Vernier:

"Sir," he would begin, "I wish to speak with you privately."

"Can it wait?" Vernier would ask.

"No, sir," he would say firmly, "as a matter of fact it is rather urgent."

Vernier would take him to an empty classroom and say, "What is troubling you, Kojo Ananse?"

"I wish to make a confession, sir. I broke the thermometer yesterday." He had decided he would not name Bandele; it was up to the latter to decide whether he would lead a pure life.

Vernier would adjust his slipping glasses up his nose and think. Then he would say:

"This is a serious matter, Kojo. You realize you should have confessed yesterday?"

"Yes, sir, I am very sorry."

"You have done great harm, but better late than never. You will, of course, apologize in front of the class and particularly to Basu who has shown himself a finer chap than all of you."

"I shall do so, sir."

"Why have you come to me now to apologize? Were you hoping that I would simply forgive you?"

"I was hoping you would, sir. I was hoping you would show your forgiveness by beating me."

Vernier would pull his glasses up his nose again. He would move his tongue inside his mouth reflectively. "I think you are right. Do you feel you deserve six strokes or nine?"

"Nine, sir."

"Bend over!"

Kojo had decided he would not cry because he was almost a man.

Whack! Whack!!

Lying in bed in the dark thinking about it all as it would happen tomorrow, he clenched his teeth and tensed his buttocks in imaginary pain.

Whack! Whack!! Whack!!!

Suddenly, in his little room, under his thin cotton sheet, he began to cry. Because he felt the sharp lancing pain already cutting into him. Because of Basu and Simpson and the thermometer. For all the things he wanted to do and be

111

which would never happen. For all the good men they had told them about, Jesus Christ, Mohammed, and George Washington who never told a lie. For Florence Nightingale and David Livingstone. For Kagawa, the Japanese man, for Gandhi, and for Kwegyir Aggrey, the African. Oh-ee, oh-ee. Because he knew he would never be as straight and strong and true as the school song said they should be. He saw, for the first time, what this thing would be like, becoming a man. He touched the edge of an inconsolable eternal grief. Oh-ee, oh-ee; always, he felt, always I shall be a disgrace to the nation and the race.

His mother passed by his bedroom door, slowly dragging her slippered feet as she always did. He pushed his face into his wet pillow to stifle his sobs, but she had heard him. She came in and switched on the light.

"What is the matter with you, my son?"

He pushed his face farther into his pillow.

"Nothing," he said, muffled and choking.

"You have been looking like a sick fowl all afternoon," she continued.

She advanced and put the back of her moist cool fingers against the side of his neck.

"You have got fever," she exclaimed. "I'll get something from the kitchen."

When she had gone out, Kojo dried his tears and turned the dry side of the pillow up. His mother reappeared with a thermometer in one hand and some quinine mixture in the other.

"Oh, take it away, take it away," he shouted, pointing to her right hand and shutting his eyes tightly.

"All right, all right," she said, slipping the thermometer into her bosom.

He is a queer boy, she thought, with pride and a little fear as she watched him drink the clear bitter fluid.

She then stood by him and held his head against her broad thigh as he sat up on the low bed, and she stroked his face. She knew he had been crying but did not ask him why, because she was sure he would not tell her. She knew he was learning, first slowly and now quickly, and she would soon cease to be his mother and be only one of the womenfolk in the family. Such a short time, she thought, when they are really yours and tell you everything. She sighed and slowly eased his sleeping head down gently.

The next day Kojo got to school early, and set to things briskly. He told Bandele that he was going to confess but would not name him. He half hoped he would join him. But Bandele had said, threateningly, that he had better not mention his name, let him go and be a Boy Scout on his own. The sneer strengthened him and he went off to the lab. He met Mr. Abu and asked for Vernier. Abu said Vernier was busy and what was the matter, anyhow.

"I broke the thermometer yesterday," Kojo said in a businesslike manner.

Abu put down the glassware he was carrying.

"Well, I never!" he said. "What do you think you will gain by this?"

"I broke it," Kojo repeated.

"Basu broke it," Abu said impatiently. "Sorie got him to confess and Basu himself came here this morning and told the science master and myself that he knew now that he had knocked the thermometer by mistake when he came in early yesterday afternoon. He had not turned round to look, but he had definitely heard a tinkle as he walked by. Someone must have picked it up and put it in the waste bin. The whole matter is settled, the palaver finished."

He tapped a barometer on the wall and, squinting, read the pressure. He turned again to Kojo.

"I should normally have expected him to say so yesterday and save you boys missing the game. But there you are," he added, shrugging and trying to look reasonable, "you cannot hope for too much from a Syrian boy."

THE SUMMER BOOK

Tove Jansson

*Ever since her mother died when she was a little girl,
Sophia, along with her father, has spent summers with her
grandmother on a wild island off the coast of Finland.*

In these three chapters from The Summer Book, *Sophia
and her grandmother talk, play, and quarrel with each other.
In "Playing Venice," they build a miniature version of the
old and beautiful Italian city by the sea; in "The Cat," they
try to find the right pet for Sophia; and in "The Robe,"
they wait for Sophia's father to sail home during a storm.*

PLAYING VENICE

One Saturday there was mail for Sophia—a picture
postcard from Venice. Her whole name was on the address
side, with "Miss" in front, and on the shiny side was the
prettiest picture anyone in the family had ever seen. There
was a long row of pink and gilded palaces rising from a
dark waterway that mirrored the lanterns on several slim

gondolas. The full moon was shining in a dark blue sky, and a beautiful, lonely woman stood on a little bridge with one hand covering her eyes. The picture was tinged with real gold here and there in appropriate places. They put the postcard up on the wall under the barometer.

Sophia wanted to know why all the buildings were standing in the water, and her grandmother told her all about Venice and how it is sinking into the sea. She had been there herself once. The memory of her trip to Italy exhilarated her, and she talked on and on. Occasionally she tried to tell about other places she had seen, but Sophia wanted only to hear about Venice, and especially about the dark canals that smelled of must and rot and that each year pulled the city farther down into the mud, down into a soft black slime where golden dinner plates lay buried. There is something very elegant about throwing the plates out the window after dinner, and about living in a house that is slowly sinking to its doom. "Look, Mama," said the lovely Venetian girl, "the kitchen is under water today." "Dear child, it doesn't matter," her mother replied. "We still have the drawing room." They rode down in their elevator and stepped into a gondola and glided through the streets. There wasn't an automobile in the entire city, they had all long since sunk into the ooze. The only sound was footsteps on the bridges, and people walked and walked all night. Sometimes one heard a strain of music, and sometimes a creaking noise as some palace settled and sank deeper. And the smell of mud was everywhere.

Sophia went down to the marsh pool, which was a smooth brownish-black under the alder trees. She dug a canal through the moss and the bilberry bushes. "Mama, my ring has fallen in the canal." Her ring was gold, with a red ruby. "Dear child, don't trouble yourself. We have the whole drawing room full of gold and precious jewels."

Sophia went to her grandmother and said, "Call me 'Dear Child' and I'll call you 'Mama.' "

"But I'm your grandmother," Grandmother said.

"Please, Mama, it's a game," Sophia explained. "Mama, shall we play you're my grandmother? I am your dear child from Venice, and I've made a canal."

Grandmother stood up. "I know a better game," she said. "We'll be old Venetians building a new Venice."

They started building in the marsh pool. They made pilings for the Piazza San Marco out of a lot of little wooden plugs, and covered them with flat stones. They dug additional canals and built bridges over them. Black ants scurried back and forth across the bridges, while down below there were gondolas gliding along in the moonlight. Sophia collected pieces of white marble along the shore.

"Look, Mama," she called. "I've found a new palace."

"But my dear child, I'm only 'Mama' to your father," Grandmother said. She was concerned.

"Is that so!" Sophia shouted. "Why is he the only one who gets to say 'Mama'?"

She threw the palace in the water and stalked away.

Grandmother sat down on the veranda to make a Doge's Palace out of balsa wood. When the palace was done, she painted it with watercolors and gold. Sophia came to look at it.

"In this palace," Grandmother said, "there lives a mother and a father and their daughter. Right through that window. The daughter has just thrown the dinner plates out the window, and they broke on the piazza, because they were only china. I wonder what the mother said."

"I know what the mother said," Sophia declared. "She said, 'My dear child, do you think there's no end to your mother's china?' "

"And what did the daughter say?"

"She said, 'Forgive me, Mama. I promise to throw only the golden dinner plates in the future!' "

They set the palace by the piazza, and the father, mother, and daughter continued to live there. Grandmother made more palaces. A great many families moved into Venice and called to one another across the canals. "How far did your palace sink today?" "Oh, it's not so bad. Mother says it's only a foot or so." "What's your mother making for dinner? My mother's boiling some perch." At night they all slept soundly, and the only noise was the footsteps of the ants across the bridges.

Grandmother became more and more involved. She made a hotel and a trattoria and a campanile with a little lion on top. It was a very long time since she'd been in Venice and she could remember the names of all the streets, because her memory was best for things that had happened long ago. One day, there was a green salamander in the Grand Canal and traffic had to make a long detour.

That same evening, it started to rain, and the wind went over to the southeast. The radio said low-pressure system and winds to thirty miles an hour, but no one gave it a second thought. But when Grandmother woke up in the middle of the night as usual, and heard rain pelting on the roof, she remembered the sinking city, and it worried her. It was blowing hard, and there was nothing but a grassy beach between the marsh and the sea. Grandmother dozed off and woke up again several times, and each time she heard the rain and the waves and worried about Venice and Sophia. When it started to get light, she got up and put on a slicker over her nightgown and covered her head with a sou'wester.

The rain had let up, but the ground was drenched and dark. It will make everything grow, she thought absent-mindedly. She took a firm grip on her walking stick and stumbled on against the wind. It was a beautiful gray dawn, with long parallel rain clouds marching across the sky and whitecaps covering the dark green sea. She could see right away that the whole shore line was flooded, and then she saw Sophia running toward her across the rock.

"It's sunk," Sophia screamed. "She's gone!"

The cottage was open, and the door stood banging in the wind.

"Go back to bed," Grandmother said. "Take off your nightgown, it's wet through, and close the door and go to bed. I'll find the palace. I promise I'll find it."

Sophia was crying with her mouth wide open. She wasn't listening. Finally Grandmother had to go with her to the cottage to be sure she went back to bed.

"I'll find the palace," she told her again. "Now stop howling and go to sleep."

She closed the door and walked back down toward the shore. When she got there, she found that the marsh had become a bay. The waves washed up into the heather and swept back into the sea again, and the alders stood well out in the water. Venice had disappeared beneath the sea.

Grandmother stood gazing at this scene for quite a while; then she turned and went home. She lit the lamp and got out her tools and a suitable piece of balsa wood and put on her glasses.

The Doge's Palace was ready at seven o'clock, just as Sophia banged on the door.

"Wait a minute," Grandmother said. "It's latched."

"Did you find her?" Sophia called. "Was she still there?"

"Yes, of course," Grandmother answered. "They were all still there."

The palace looked much too new, not as if it had been through a flood. Quickly Grandmother took her water glass and poured it over the Doge's Palace, then emptied the ashtray into her hand and rubbed the cupolas and walls with ashes, and all the time Sophia kept pulling at the handle and yelling that she wanted in.

Grandmother opened the door. "We were lucky," she said.

Sophia examined the palace very carefully. She put it down on the night stand and didn't say a word.

"It's all right, isn't it?" said Grandmother anxiously.

"Quiet," Sophia whispered. "I want to hear if she's still there."

They listened for a long time. Then Sophia said, "You can rest easy. Her mother says it was a perfectly dreadful storm. Now she's cleaning up the mess, and she's pretty worn out."

"Yes, I'll bet she is," Grandmother said.

THE CAT

It was a tiny kitten when it came and could drink its milk only from a nipple. Fortunately, they still had Sophia's baby bottle in the attic. In the beginning, the kitten slept in a tea cozy to keep warm, but when it found its legs they let it sleep in the cottage in Sophia's bed. It had its own pillow, next to hers.

It was a gray fisherman's cat and it grew fast. One day, it left the cottage and moved into the house, where it spent its nights under the bed in the box where they kept the dirty dishes. It had odd ideas of its own even then. Sophia carried the cat back to the cottage and tried as hard as she could to ingratiate herself, but the more love she gave it, the quicker it fled back to the dish box. When the box got too full, the cat would howl and someone would have to wash the dishes. Its name was Ma Petite, but they called it Moppy.

"It's funny about love," Sophia said. "The more you love someone, the less he likes you back."

"That's very true," Grandmother observed. "And so what do you do?"

"You go on loving," said Sophia threateningly. "You love harder and harder."

Her grandmother sighed and said nothing.

Moppy was carried around to all the pleasant places a cat might like, and he only glanced at them and walked away. He was flattened with hugs, endured them politely, and climbed back into the dish box. He was entrusted with burning secrets and merely averted his yellow gaze. Nothing in the world seemed to interest this cat but food and sleep.

"You know," Sophia said, "sometimes I think I hate Moppy. I don't have the strength to go on loving him, but I think about him all the time!"

Week after week, Sophia pursued the cat. She spoke softly and gave him comfort and understanding, and only a couple of times did she lose her patience and yell at him, or pull his tail. At such times Moppy would hiss and run under the house, and afterward his appetite was better and he slept even longer than usual, curled up in unapproachable softness with one paw daintily across his nose.

Sophia stopped playing and started having nightmares. She couldn't think about anything but this cat who refused to be affectionate. Meanwhile, Moppy grew into a lean and wild little animal, and one June night he didn't come back to his dish box. In the morning, he walked into the house and stretched—front legs first, with his rear end up in the air—then he closed his eyes and sharpened his claws on the rocking chair, after which he jumped up on the bed and went to sleep. The cat's whole being radiated calm superiority.

He's started hunting, Grandmother thought.

She was right. The very next morning, the cat came in and placed a small grayish-yellow bird on the doorsill. Its neck had been deftly broken with one bite, and some bright red drops of blood lay prettily on the shiny coat of feathers. Sophia turned pale and stared fixedly at the murdered bird. She sidled past Moppy, the murderer, with small, forced steps, and then turned and rushed out.

Later, Grandmother remarked on the curious fact that wild animals, cats for example, cannot understand the difference between a rat and a bird.

"Then they're dumb!" said Sophia curtly. "Rats are hideous, and birds are nice. I don't think I'll talk to Moppy for three days." And she stopped talking to her cat.

Every night, the cat went into the woods, and every morning it killed its prey and carried it into the house to be admired, and every morning the bird was thrown into the sea. A little while later, Sophia would appear outside the window and shout, "Can I come in? Have you taken out the body?" She punished Moppy and increased her own pain by means of a terrible coarseness. "Have you cleaned up the blood?" she would yell, or, "How many murdered today?" And morning coffee was no longer what it had been.

It was a great relief when Moppy finally learned to conceal his crimes. It is one thing to see a pool of blood and quite another thing only to know about it. Moppy probably grew tired of all the screaming and fussing, and perhaps he thought the family ate his birds. One morning when Grandmother was taking her first cigarette on the veranda, she dropped her holder and it rolled through a crack in the floor. She managed to raise one of the planks, and there was Moppy's handiwork—a row of small bird skeletons, all picked clean. Of course she knew that the cat had continued to hunt, and could not have stopped, but the next time he rubbed against her leg as he passed, she drew away and whispered, "You sly bastard." The cat dish stood, untouched, by the steps and attracted flies.

"You know what?" Sophia said. "I wish Moppy had never been born. Or else that I'd never been born. That would have been better."

"So you're still not speaking to each other?" Grandmother asked.

"Not a word," Sophia said. "I don't know what to do. And if I do forgive him—what fun is that when he doesn't even care?" Grandmother couldn't think of anything to say.

Moppy turned wild and rarely came into the house. He was the same color as the island—a light yellowish-gray with striped shadings like granite, or like sunlight on a sand bottom. When he slipped across the meadow by the beach, his progress was like a stroke of wind through the grass. He would watch for hours in the thicket, a motionless silhouette, two pointed ears against the sunset, and then suddenly vanish . . . and some bird would chirp, just once. He would slink under the creeping pines, soaked by the rain and lean as a streak, and he would wash himself voluptuously when the sun came out. He was an absolutely happy cat, but he didn't share with anyone. On hot days, he would roll on the smooth rock, and sometimes he would eat grass and calmly vomit his own hair the way cats do. And what he did between times no one knew.

One Saturday, the Övergårds came for coffee. Sophia went down to look at their boat. It was big, full of bags and jerry cans and baskets, and in one of the baskets a cat was meowing. Sophia lifted the lid and the cat licked her hand. It was a big, white cat with a broad face. It kept right on purring when she picked it up and carried it ashore.

"So you found the cat," said Anna Övergård. "It's a nice cat, but it's not a mouser, so we thought we'd give it to some friends."

Sophia sat on the bed with the heavy cat on her lap. It never stopped purring. It was soft and warm and submissive.

They struck a bargain easily, with a bottle of rum to close the deal. Moppy was captured and never knew what was happening until the Övergård's boat was on its way to town.

The new cat's name was Fluff. It ate fish and liked to be petted. It moved into Sophia's cottage and slept every night in her arms, and every morning it came in to morning coffee and slept some more in the bed beside the stove. If the sun was shining, it would roll on the warm granite.

"Not there!" Sophia yelled. "That's Moppy's place!" She carried the cat a little farther off, and it licked her on the nose and rolled obediently in the new spot.

The summer grew prettier and prettier, a long series of calm blue summer days. Every night, Fluff slept against Sophia's cheek.

"It's funny about me," Sophia said. "I think nice weather gets to be boring."

"Do you?" her grandmother said. "Then you're just like your grandfather, he liked storms too." But before she could say anything else about Grandfather, Sophia was gone.

And gradually the wind came up, sometime during the night, and by morning there was a regular southwester spitting foam all over the rocks.

"Wake up," Sophia whispered. "Wake up, kitty, precious, there's a storm."

Fluff purred and stretched warm sleepy legs in all directions. The sheet was covered with cat hair.

"Get up!" Sophia shouted. "It's a storm!" But the cat just turned over on its broad stomach. And suddenly Sophia was furious. She kicked open the door and threw the cat out in the wind and watched how it laid its ears back, and she screamed, "Hunt! Do something! Be like a cat!" And then she started to cry and ran to the guest room and banged on the door.

"What's wrong now?" Grandmother said.

"I want Moppy back!" Sophia screamed.

"But you know how it'll be," Grandmother said.

"It'll be awful," said Sophia gravely. "But it's Moppy I love."

And so they traded cats again.

THE ROBE

Sophia's father had a special bathrobe that he loved. It reached all the way to his feet and was made of very thick, stiff flannel that salt water, soil, and time had rendered even stiffer. The robe was probably German, originally, and had once been green. On its front, it still bore the remains of an intricate system of laces, along with a couple of large dark amber buttons. Thrown wide open, the robe was as broad as a tent.

In the beginning, when Papa was a young man, he used to sit out on the point in his bathrobe whenever it stormed and watch the waves. Later, it was nice to put on when he wanted to work or get warm, or simply hide.

The robe had survived various threats to its existence. There was the time some well-meaning relatives came out and, as a surprise, gave the island a good cleaning. They threw out a lot of things the family wanted, but, worst of all, they carried the bathrobe down to the water and let it float away. They claimed later that it smelled. Of course it smelled—that was part of its charm. Smell is important. It reminds a person of all the things he's been through; it is a sheath of memories and security. The robe smelled of good things, too—of smoke and the sea—but maybe they never noticed that. In any case, the robe came back. The wind blew, shifted, and reversed, the waves beat against the island, and one fine day they brought it home. After that, it smelled of seaweed, and Papa wore virtually nothing else that whole summer. Then there was the spring when they discovered a family of mice had been living in the robe. The collar was edged with a soft, downy material that the mice had nibbled off and used for bedclothes, along with some finely chewed handkerchiefs. And then one time Papa slept too close to the fire and the robe was scorched.

When Papa got a little older, he put the bathrobe up in the attic. He would go up there to think sometimes, and the others always took it for granted that he did his thinking in the robe. It lay under one of the little attic windows, long and dark and mysterious.

Sophia went through a rebellious phase one cold, rainy summer when being unhappy outdoors was a lot of trouble. So she would go up in the attic to be alone. She would sit in a cardboard box and stare at the robe, and she would say dreadful, crushing things, and it was hard for the robe to talk back.

In between times, she played cards with her grandmother. They both cheated shamelessly, and their card-playing afternoons always ended in a quarrel. This had never happened before. Grandmother tried to recall her own rebellious periods in order to try and understand, but all she could remember was an unusually well-behaved little girl. Wise as she was, she realized that people can postpone their rebellious phases until they're eighty-five years old, and she decided to keep an eye on herself. It rained constantly, and Papa worked from morning to night with his back to the room. They never knew if he was listening to them or not.

"Jesus," Sophia said. "There you sit with the King and you don't say anything!"

"Don't take the name of the Lord in vain," Grandmother said.

"I didn't say 'God,' I said 'Jesus.' "

"He's just as important as God is."

"He isn't either!"

"Of course he is!"

Sophia threw her cards on the floor and yelled, "I don't care about His old family! I hate families!" She clambered up the attic stairs and slammed the trapdoor behind her.

The attic was so low that there was only room to crawl. And if you didn't crawl carefully, you would hit your head on the rafters. It was also very crowded—just one narrow path through all the things being kept and saved and forgotten, all the things that had always been there and that not even the well-meaning relatives had found. The path led from the south window to the north window, and the roof between the rafters was painted blue. Sophia had no flashlight, and it was dark. The path was an endless, empty street in the moonlight between shaggy houses. At the end of the street was the window with its moon-white sky, and beneath the window lay the robe, a pile of stiff folds, coal-black in its own shadow. Sophia had slammed the trapdoor with such a bang that she couldn't retreat. And so she crept over and sat down in her cardboard box. The bathrobe lay with one sleeve thrown forward across its gaping neck. She stared at it, and as she stared the sleeve rose just a trifle, and a tiny movement crept in under the robe and down toward the foot end. The folds altered imperceptibly, and the robe was still again. But she had seen it. There, inside the robe, there was something alive—or else the whole robe was alive. Sophia resorted to the simplest means of flight available in cases of great distress: she fell asleep. She was still asleep when they put her to bed, but in the morning she knew that there was danger in the robe. No one else must know. She kept the amazing truth to herself, and for several days she was almost elated. The rain had stopped. She drew pictures with shaggy shadows and made the moon very tiny, forgotten in a huge dark sky. She showed these pictures to no one. The danger dwelt in a fold deep down inside. It moved about at times and then crept back. When frightened, it showed its teeth, and it was far more dangerous than death.

Every day when the sun went down, Sophia would climb up the ladder, poke her nose through the trapdoor, and peer into the attic. She could see one little corner of the bathrobe if she craned her neck.

"What are you doing?" Grandmother asked.

"None of your business, nosey!" Sophia whined in her most irritating voice.

"Close the trapdoor. There's a draft," Grandmother said. "Go do something outside." She turned toward the wall and went on with her book. They had both become impossible and couldn't get along at all. They quarreled the wrong way. The days were cloudy, with rising winds, and Papa just sat at his desk and worked.

Sophia thought about the bathrobe more and more. The thing living in it was as quick as lightning but could lie in wait for days without moving. It could make itself thin and slide through a crack in the door, and then roll itself up again and crawl under the bed like a shadow. It didn't eat and never slept and hated everyone, most of all its own family. Sophia didn't eat either, that is, nothing but sandwiches.

It may not really have been her fault, but one day they ran out of bread and butter, and Papa took the boat in to the store to get supplies. He put the water jug in the boat, and the cans for kerosene and gasoline, and he took the shopping list from the wall and left. There was a southwest wind when he set out, and in a couple of hours it had risen so that the waves were riding right across the point. Grandmother tried to get the weather report on the radio, but she couldn't find the right button. She couldn't keep from going back to the north window every few minutes to look for him, and she didn't understand a word she read.

Sophia went down to the shore, and came back and sat down at the table. "And all you can do is just read," she said. She raised her voice and screamed, "You just read and read and read!" Then she threw herself down on the table and wept.

Grandmother sat up and said, "He'll make it all right." She was feeling a little ill and felt for the Lupatro behind the curtain. Sophia went on crying, but she kept an eye on Grandmother under her arm. "I don't feel good either," she screamed, and jumped up and vomited on the rug. Then she was quiet and pale and sat down on the bed.

"Lie down," Grandmother said, and she lay down. They both lay down and listened to the wind outside as it attacked in short, violent bursts.

"Once you get to the village," Grandmother said, "it always takes a long time at the store. There's always a line, and no one's in a hurry. And then the boy has to go down to the dock and fill you up with gasoline and kerosene. And you have to go pick up the mail, and sort through it to find what's for you. And if there's a money order you have to go in and get it stamped, and that means a cup of coffee. And then he has to pay the bills. It can take a long time."

"Go on," Sophia said.

"Well, then he has to take everything down to the boat," Grandmother said. "He has to pack it all in and cover it so it won't get wet. And on the way down he remembers to pick some flowers, and give some bread to the horse. And the bread's way down at the bottom of a bag somewhere . . ."

131

"I shouldn't have eaten so many sandwiches!" Sophia wailed and started to cry again. "I'm cold!"

Grandmother tried to cover her with a blanket, but the child kicked it off and flailed her legs and screamed that she hated all of them.

"Quiet!" Grandmother yelled. "Quiet down! Or I'll throw up on you." Sophia stopped screaming immediately. There was a moment's silence, and then she said, "I want the bathrobe."

"But it's up in the attic," Grandmother said.

"I want it," her grandchild said.

And so Grandmother climbed the attic ladder. It went fine. She crawled over to the window for the robe and dragged it back to the trapdoor. Then she dropped it down into the room and sat and rested for a while, dangling her feet over the edge. She hadn't been up there for a very long time, and she read the labels on the boxes. String. Tackle. Bottles. All kinds of things. Rags and old trousers. She had printed the labels herself. They had painted the ceiling blue, but they hadn't put enough glue in the paint; it was flaking.

"What are you doing?" Sophia yelled. "Don't you feel good?"

"Yes," Grandmother answered through the trap. "I feel better." She lowered one leg very cautiously and found the step. Then she turned slowly over on her stomach and brought down the other leg.

"Take it easy!" Sophia called from down below. She saw Grandmother's stiff old legs move from one step to the next and finally reach the floor. Grandmother picked up the robe and came over to the bed.

"You have to shake it first," Sophia said. "And make it come out."

Grandmother didn't understand, but she shook the robe. It came slinking out one sleeve and disappeared under the door. The robe smelled the same as before. It was very heavy, and became a warm, dark cave. Sophia fell asleep right away, and Grandmother sat down in the north window to wait. It was blowing hard, and the sun was setting. She was far-sighted and saw the boat half an hour before it reached the island—a moustache of white foam that would appear at irregular intervals and sometimes vanish entirely.

When the boat reached the shelter of the island, she lay down on the bed and closed her eyes. A few minutes later, Sophia's father came into the room. He was wet through. He put down the bags and lit his pipe. Then he took the lamp and went out to fill it with kerosene.

THE ALLIGATORS

John Updike

Joan Edison came to their half of the fifth grade from Maryland in March. She had a thin face with something of a grownup's tired expression and long black eyelashes like a doll's. Everybody hated her. That month Miss Fritz was reading to them during homeroom about a girl, Emmy, who was badly spoiled and always telling her parents lies about her twin sister Annie; nobody could believe, it was too amazing, how exactly when they were despising Emmy most Joan should come into the school with her show-off clothes and her hair left hanging down the back of her fuzzy sweater instead of being cut or braided and her having the crust to actually argue with teachers. "Well I'm sorry," she told Miss Fritz, not even rising from her seat, "but I *don't* see what the point is of homework. In Baltimore we never had any, and the *little* kids there knew what's in these books."

Charlie, who in a way enjoyed homework, was ready to join in the angry moan of the others. Little hurt lines had leaped up between Miss Fritz's eyebrows and he felt sorry for her, remembering how when that September John Eberly had half on purpose spilled purple Sho-Card paint on the newly sandpapered floor she had hidden her face in her arms on the desk and cried. She was afraid of the school board. "You're not in Baltimore now, Joan," Miss Fritz said. "You are in Olinger, Pennsylvania."

The children, Charlie among them, laughed, and Joan, blushing a soft brown color and raising her voice excitedly against the current of hatred, got in deeper by trying to explain, "Like there, instead of just *reading* about plants in a book we'd one day all bring in a flower we'd *picked* and cut it open and look at it in a *microscope*." Because of her saying this, shadows, of broad leaves and wild slashed foreign flowers, darkened and complicated the idea they had of her.

Miss Fritz puckered her orange lips into fine wrinkles, then smiled. "In the upper levels you will be allowed to do that in this school. All things come in time, Joan, to patient little girls." When Joan started to argue *this,* Miss Fritz lifted one finger and said with the extra weight adults always have, held back in reserve, "No. No more, young lady, or you'll be in *serious* trouble with me." It gave the class courage to see that Miss Fritz didn't like her either.

After that, Joan couldn't open her mouth in class without there being a great groan. Outdoors on the macadam playground, at recess or fire drill or waiting in the morning for the buzzer, hardly anybody talked to her except to say "Stuck-up" or "Emmy" or "Whore, whore, from Balti-more." Boys were always yanking open the bow at the back of her fancy dresses and flipping little spitballs into the curls of her hanging hair. Once John Eberly even cut a section of her hair off with a yellow plastic scissors stolen from art class. This was the one time Charlie saw Joan cry actual tears. He was as bad as the others: worse, because what the others did because they felt like it, he did out of a plan, to make himself more popular. In the first and second grade he had been liked pretty well, but somewhere since then he had been dropped. There was a gang, boys and girls both, that met Saturdays—you heard them talk about it on Mondays—in Stuart Morrison's garage, and took hikes and played touch football together, and in winter sledded on Hill Street, and in spring bicycled all over Olinger and did together what else, he couldn't imagine. Charlie had known the chief members since before kindergarten. But after school there seemed nothing for him to do but go home promptly and do his homework and fiddle with his Central American stamps and go to horror movies alone, and on weekends nothing but beat monotonously at marbles or Monopoly or chess Darryl Johns or Marvin Auerbach, who he wouldn't have bothered at all with if they hadn't lived right in the neighborhood, they being at least a year younger and not bright for their age, either. Charlie thought the gang might notice him and take him in if he backed up their policies without being asked.

In Science, which 5A had in Miss Brobst's room across the hall, he sat one seat ahead of Joan and annoyed her all he could, in spite of a feeling that, both being disliked, they had something to share. One fact he discovered was, she wasn't that bright. Her marks on quizzes were always lower than his. He told her, "Cutting up all those flowers didn't do you much good. Or maybe in Baltimore they taught you everything so long ago you've forgotten it in your old age."

Charlie drew; on his tablet where she could easily see over his shoulder he once in a while drew a picture titled "Joan the Dope": the profile of a girl with a lean nose and sad mincemouth, the lashes of her lowered eye as black as the pencil could make them and the hair falling, in ridiculous hooks, row after row, down through the sea-blue cross-lines clear off the bottom edge of the tablet.

March turned into spring. One of the signals was, on the high school grounds, before the cinder track was weeded and when the softball field was still four inches of mud, Happy Lasker came with the elaborate airplane model he had wasted the winter making. It had the American star on the wingtips and a pilot painted inside the cockpit and a miniature motor that burned real gas. The buzzing, off and on all Saturday morning, collected smaller kids from Second Street down to Lynoak. Then it was always the same: Happy shoved the plane into the air, where it climbed and made a razzing noise a minute, then nose-dived and crashed and usually burned in the grass or mud. Happy's father was rich.

In the weeks since she had come, Joan's clothes had slowly grown simpler, to go with the other girls', and one

137

day she came to school with most of her hair cut off, and the rest brushed flat around her head and brought into a little tail behind. The laughter at her was more than she had ever heard. "Ooh. Baldy-paldy!" some idiot girl had exclaimed when Joan came into the cloakroom, and the stupid words went sliding around class all morning. "Baldy-paldy from Baltimore. Why is old Baldy-paldy red in the face?" John Eberly kept making the motion of a scissors with his fingers and its juicy ticking sound with his tongue. Miss Fritz rapped her knuckles on the window sill until she was rubbing the ache with the other hand, and finally she sent two boys to Mr. Lengel's office, delighting Charlie an enormous secret amount.

His own reaction to the haircut had been quiet, to want to draw her, changed. He had kept the other drawings folded in his desk, and one of his instincts was toward complete sets of things, Batman comics and A's and Costa Rican stamps. Halfway across the room from him, Joan held very still, afraid, it seemed, to move even a hand, her face a shamed pink. The haircut had brought out her forehead and exposed her neck and made her chin pointier and her eyes larger. Charlie felt thankful once again for having been born a boy, and having no sharp shocks, like losing your curls or starting to bleed, to make growing painful. How much girls suffer had been one of the first thoughts he had ever had. His caricature of her was wonderful, the work of a genius. He showed it to Stuart Morrison behind him; it was too good for him to appreciate, his dull egg eyes just flickered over it. Charlie traced it onto another piece of tablet paper, making her

head completely bald. This drawing Stuart grabbed and it
was passed clear around the room.

That night he had the dream. He must have dreamed it
while lying there asleep in the morning light, for it was
fresh in his head when he woke. They had been in a jungle.
Joan, dressed in a torn sarong, was swimming in a clear
river among alligators. Somehow, as if from a tree, he was
looking down, and there was a calmness in the way the slim
girl and the green alligators moved, in and out, perfectly
visible under the window-skin of the water. Joan's face
sometimes showed the horror she was undergoing and
sometimes looked numb. Her hair trailed behind and
fanned when her face came toward the surface. He shouted
silently with grief. Then he had rescued her; without a
sense of having dipped his arms in water, he was carrying
her in two arms, himself in a bathing suit, and his feet
firmly fixed to the knobby back of an alligator which
skimmed upstream, through the shadows of high trees and
white flowers and hanging vines, like a surfboard in a
movie short. They seemed to be heading toward a wooden
bridge arching over the stream. He wondered how he
would duck it, and the river and the jungle gave way to his
bed and his room, but through the change persisted, like a
pedaled note on a piano, the sweetness and pride he had
felt in saving and carrying the girl.

He loved Joan Edison. The morning was rainy, and
under the umbrella his mother made him take this new
knowledge, repeated again and again to himself, gathered
like a bell of smoke. Love had no taste, but sharpened his

sense of smell so that his oilcloth coat, his rubber boots, the red-tipped bushes hanging over the low walls holding back lawns all along Grand Street, even the dirt and moss in the cracks of the pavement each gave off clear odors. He would have laughed, if a wooden weight had not been placed high in his chest, near where his throat joined. He could not imagine himself laughing soon. It seemed he had reached one of those situations his Sunday school teacher, poor Miss West with her little mustache, had been trying to prepare him for. He prayed, *Give me Joan.* With the wet weather a solemn flatness had fallen over everything; an orange bus turning at the Bend and four birds on a telephone wire seemed to have the same importance. Yet he felt firmer and lighter and felt things as edges he must whip around and channels he must rush down. If he carried her off, did rescue her from the others' cruelty, he would have defied the gang and made a new one, his own. Just Joan and he at first, then others escaping from meanness and dumbness, until his gang was stronger and Stuart Morrison's garage was empty every Saturday. Charlie would be a king, with his own touch football game. Everyone would come and plead with him for mercy.

His first step was to tell all those in the cloakroom he loved Joan Edison now. They cared less than he had expected, considering how she was hated. He had more or less expected to have to fight with his fists. Hardly anybody gathered to hear the dream he had pictured himself telling everybody. Anyway that morning it would go around the class that he said he loved her, and though this was what he wanted, to in a way open a space between him and Joan, it felt funny nevertheless, and he stuttered when Miss Fritz had him go to the blackboard to explain something.

At lunch, he deliberately hid in the variety store until he saw her walk by. The homely girl with her he knew turned off at the next street. He waited a minute and then came out and began running to overtake Joan in the block between the street where the other girl turned down and the street where he turned up. It had stopped raining, and his rolled-up umbrella felt like a commando's bayonet. Coming up behind her, he said, "Bang. Bang."

She turned, and under her gaze, knowing she knew he loved her, his face heated and he stared down. "Why, Charlie," her voice said with her Maryland slowness, "what are you doing on this side of the street?" Carl the town cop stood in front of the elementary school to get them on the side of Grand Street where they belonged. Now Charlie would have to cross the avenue again, by himself, at the dangerous five-spoked intersection.

"Nothing," he said, and used up the one sentence he had prepared ahead: "I like your hair the new way."

"Thank you," she said, and stopped. In Baltimore she must have had manner lessons. Her eyes looked at his, and his vision jumped back from the rims of her lower lids as if from a brink. Yet in the space she occupied there was a great fullness that lent him height, as if he were standing by a window giving on the first morning after a snow.

"But then I didn't mind it the old way either."

"Yes?"

A peculiar reply. Another peculiar thing was the tan beneath her skin; he had noticed before, though not so closely, how when she colored it came up a gentle dull brown more than red. Also she wore something perfumed.

He asked, "How do you like Olinger?"

"Oh, I think it's nice."

"Nice? I guess. I guess maybe. Nice Olinger. I wouldn't know because I've never been anywhere else."

She luckily took this as a joke and laughed. Rather than risk saying something unfunny, he began to balance the umbrella by its point on one finger and, when this went well, walked backwards, shifting the balanced umbrella, its hook black against the patchy blue sky, from one palm to the other, back and forth. At the corner where they parted he got carried away and in imitating a suave gent leaning on a cane bent the handle hopelessly. Her amazement was worth twice the price of his mother's probable crossness.

He planned to walk her again, and further, after school. All through lunch he kept calculating. His father and he would repaint his bike. At the next haircut he would have his hair parted on the other side to get away from his cowlick. He would change himself totally; everyone would wonder what had happened to him. He would learn to swim, and take her to the dam.

In the afternoon the momentum of the dream wore off somewhat. Now that he kept his eyes always on her, he noticed, with a qualm of his stomach, that in passing in the afternoon from Miss Brobst's to Miss Fritz's room, Joan was not alone, but chattered with others. In class, too, she whispered. So it was with more shame—such shame that he didn't believe he could ever face even his parents again—than surprise that from behind the dark pane of the variety store he saw her walk by in the company of the gang, she and Stuart Morrison throwing back their teeth and screaming and he imitating something and poor moronic John Eberly tagging behind like a thick tail. Charlie watched them walk out of sight behind a tall hedge; relief was as yet a tiny fraction of his reversed world. It came to him that what he had taken for cruelty had been love, that far from hating her everybody had loved her from the beginning, and that even the stupidest knew it weeks before he did. That she was the queen of the class and might as well not exist, for all the good he would get out of it.

TWEEDLEDUM AND TWEEDLEDEE

Lewis Carroll

*Seven-and-a-half-year-old Alice dreams that she walks
"through the looking-glass" in her drawing room and enters a
world where elements from her familiar, everyday existence
appear in strange new forms and combinations. She discovers
that Looking-glass Land is marked out like an enormous
chessboard, and that "a great huge game of chess" is being
played all over the world. Allowed to join the game as a pawn,
Alice is given directions for journeying across the board to
the last square, where she will become a queen. Along the way,
she has a series of bizarre encounters with chess pieces and
nursery rhyme characters who have come to life. In the
fourth square, she meets "two little fat men," Tweedledum
and Tweedledee.*

They were standing under a tree, each with an arm round the other's neck, and Alice knew which was which in a moment, because one of them had 'DUM' embroidered on his collar, and the other 'DEE.' "I suppose they've each got 'TWEEDLE' round at the back of the collar," she said to herself.

They stood so still that she quite forgot they were alive, and she was just looking round to see if the word 'TWEEDLE' was written at the back of each collar, when she was startled by a voice coming from the one marked 'DUM.'

"If you think we're wax-works," he said, "you ought to pay, you know. Wax-works weren't made to be looked at for nothing. Nohow!"

"Contrariwise," added the one marked 'DEE,' "if you think we're alive, you ought to speak."

"I'm sure I'm very sorry," was all Alice could say; for the words of the old song kept ringing through her head like the ticking of a clock, and she could hardly help saying them out loud:

> "Tweedledum and Tweedledee
> Agreed to have a battle;
> For Tweedledum said Tweedledee
> Had spoiled his nice new rattle.
>
> Just then flew down a monstrous crow,
> As black as a tar-barrel;
> Which frightened both the heroes so,
> They quite forgot their quarrel."

"I know what you're thinking about," said Tweedledum: "but it isn't so, nohow."

"Contrariwise," continued Tweedledee, "if it was so, it might be; and if it were so, it would be; but as it isn't, it ain't. That's logic."

"I was thinking," Alice said very politely, "which is the best way out of this wood: it's getting so dark. Would you tell me, please?"

But the fat little men only looked at each other and grinned.

They looked so exactly like a couple of great schoolboys, that Alice couldn't help pointing her finger at Tweedledum, and saying "First Boy!"

"Nohow!" Tweedledum cried out briskly, and shut his mouth up again with a snap.

"Next Boy!" said Alice, passing on to Tweedledee, though she felt quite certain he would only shout out "Contrariwise!" and so he did.

"You've begun wrong!" cried Tweedledum. "The first thing in a visit is to say 'How d'ye do?' and shake hands!" And here the two brothers gave each other a hug, and then they held out the two hands that were free, to shake hands with her.

Alice did not like shaking hands with either of them first, for fear of hurting the other one's feelings; so, as the best way out of the difficulty, she took hold of both hands at once: the next moment they were dancing round in a ring. This seemed quite natural (she remembered afterwards), and she was not even surprised to hear music playing: it seemed to come from the tree under which they were dancing, and it was done (as well as she could make it out) by the branches rubbing one across the other, like fiddles and fiddle-sticks.

"But it certainly *was* funny," (Alice said afterwards, when she was telling her sister the history of all this) "to find myself singing *'Here we go round the mulberry bush.'* I don't know when I began it, but somehow I felt as if I'd been singing it a long long time!"

The other two dancers were fat, and very soon out of breath. "Four times round is enough for one dance," Tweedledum panted out, and they left off dancing as suddenly as they had begun: the music stopped at the same moment.

Then they let go of Alice's hands, and stood looking at her for a minute: there was a rather awkward pause, as Alice didn't know how to begin a conversation with people she had just been dancing with. "It would never do to say 'How d'ye do?' *now*," she said to herself: "we seem to have got beyond that, somehow!"

"I hope you're not much tired?" she said at last.

"Nohow. And thank you *very* much for asking," said Tweedledum.

"So *much* obliged!" added Tweedledee. "You like poetry?"

"Ye-es, pretty well—*some* poetry," Alice said doubtfully. "Would you tell me which road leads out of the wood?"

"What shall I repeat to her?" said Tweedledee, looking round at Tweedledum with great solemn eyes, and not noticing Alice's question.

" *'The Walrus and the Carpenter'* is the longest," Tweedledum replied, giving his brother an affectionate hug.

Tweedledee began instantly:

> "The sun was shining—"

Here Alice ventured to interrupt him. "If it's *very* long," she said, as politely as she could, "would you please tell me first which road—"

Tweedledee smiled gently, and began again:

> "The sun was shining on the sea,
>   Shining with all his might:
> He did his very best to make
>   The billows smooth and bright—
> And this was odd, because it was
>   The middle of the night.

The moon was shining sulkily,
   Because she thought the sun
Had got no business to be there
   After the day was done—
'It's very rude of him,' she said,
   'To come and spoil the fun!'

The sea was wet as wet could be,
   The sands were dry as dry.
You could not see a cloud, because
   No cloud was in the sky:
No birds were flying overhead—
   There were no birds to fly.

The Walrus and the Carpenter
   Were walking close at hand;
They wept like anything to see
   Such quantities of sand:
'If this were only cleared away,'
   They said, 'it *would* be grand!'

'If seven maids with seven mops
   Swept it for half a year,
Do you suppose,' the Walrus said,
   'That they could get it clear?'
'I doubt it,' said the Carpenter,
   And shed a bitter tear.

'O Oysters, come and walk with us!'
    The Walrus did beseech.
'A pleasant walk, a pleasant talk,
    Along the briny beach:
We cannot do with more than four,
    To give a hand to each.'

The eldest Oyster looked at him,
    But never a word he said:
The eldest Oyster winked his eye,
    And shook his heavy head—
Meaning to say he did not choose
    To leave the oyster-bed.

But four young Oysters hurried up,
    All eager for the treat:
Their coats were brushed, their faces washed,
    Their shoes were clean and neat—
And this was odd, because, you know,
    They hadn't any feet.

Four other Oysters followed them,
    And yet another four;
And thick and fast they came at last,
    And more, and more, and more—
All hopping through the frothy waves,
    And scrambling to the shore.

The Walrus and the Carpenter
    Walked on a mile or so,
And then they rested on a rock
    Conveniently low:
And all the little Oysters stood
    And waited in a row.

'The time has come,' the Walrus said,
    'To talk of many things:
Of shoes—and ships—and sealing-wax—
    Of cabbages—and kings—
And why the sea is boiling hot—
    And whether pigs have wings.'

'But wait a bit,' the Oysters cried,
    'Before we have our chat;
For some of us are out of breath,
    And all of us are fat!'
'No hurry!' said the Carpenter.
    They thanked him much for that.

'A loaf of bread,' the Walrus said,
    'Is what we chiefly need:
Pepper and vinegar besides
    Are very good indeed—
Now if you're ready, Oysters dear,
    We can begin to feed.'

'But not on us!' the Oysters cried,
    Turning a little blue.
'After such kindness, that would be
    A dismal thing to do!'
'The night is fine,' the Walrus said.
    'Do you admire the view?

'It was so kind of you to come!
  And you are very nice!'
The Carpenter said nothing but
  'Cut us another slice:
I wish you were not quite so deaf—
  I've had to ask you twice!'

'It seems a shame,' the Walrus said,
  'To play them such a trick,
After we've brought them out so far,
  And made them trot so quick!'
The Carpenter said nothing but
  'The butter's spread too thick!'

'I weep for you,' the Walrus said:
  'I deeply sympathize.'
With sobs and tears he sorted out
  Those of the largest size,
Holding his pocket-handkerchief
  Before his streaming eyes.

'O Oysters,' said the Carpenter,
  'You've had a pleasant run!
Shall we be trotting home again?'
  But answer came there none—
And this was scarcely odd, because
  They'd eaten every one."

"I like the Walrus best," said Alice: "because you see he was a *little* sorry for the poor oysters."

"He ate more than the Carpenter, though," said Tweedledee. "You see he held his handkerchief in front, so that the Carpenter couldn't count how many he took: contrariwise."

"That was mean!" Alice said indignantly. "Then I like the Carpenter best—if he didn't eat so many as the Walrus."

"But he ate as many as he could get," said Tweedledum.

This was a puzzler. After a pause, Alice began, "Well! They were *both* very unpleasant characters—" Here she checked herself in some alarm, at hearing something that sounded to her like the puffing of a large steam-engine in the wood near them, though she feared it was more likely to be a wild beast. "Are there any lions or tigers about here?" she asked timidly.

"It's only the Red King snoring," said Tweedledee.

"Come and look at him!" the brothers cried, and they each took one of Alice's hands, and led her up to where the King was sleeping.

"Isn't he a *lovely* sight?" said Tweedledum.

Alice couldn't say honestly that he was. He had a tall red night-cap on, with a tassel, and he was lying crumpled up into a sort of untidy heap, and snoring loud—"fit to snore his head off!" as Tweedledum remarked.

"I'm afraid he'll catch cold with lying on the damp grass," said Alice, who was a very thoughtful little girl.

"He's dreaming now," said Tweedledee: "and what do you think he's dreaming about?"

Alice said "Nobody can guess that."

"Why, about *you*!" Tweedledee exclaimed, clapping his hands triumphantly. "And if he left off dreaming about you, where do you suppose you'd be?"

"Where I am now, of course," said Alice.

"Not you!" Tweedledee retorted contemptuously. "You'd be nowhere. Why, you're only a sort of thing in his dream!"

"If that there King was to wake," added Tweedledum, "you'd go out—bang!—just like a candle!"

"I shouldn't!" Alice exclaimed indignantly. "Besides, if *I'm* only a sort of thing in his dream, what are *you*, I should like to know?"

"Ditto," said Tweedledum.

"Ditto, ditto!" cried Tweedledee.

He shouted this so loud that Alice couldn't help saying, "Hush! You'll be waking him, I'm afraid, if you make so much noise."

"Well, it's no use *your* talking about waking him," said Tweedledum, "when you're only one of the things in his dream. You know very well you're not real."

"I *am* real!" said Alice, and began to cry.

"You won't make yourself a bit realler by crying," Tweedledee remarked: "there's nothing to cry about."

"If I wasn't real," Alice said—half-laughing through her tears, it all seemed so ridiculous—"I shouldn't be able to cry."

"I hope you don't suppose those are real tears?" Tweedledum interrupted in a tone of great contempt.

"I know they're talking nonsense," Alice thought to herself: "and it's foolish to cry about it." So she brushed away her tears, and went on as cheerfully as she could, "At any rate I'd better be getting out of the wood, for really it's coming on very dark. Do you think it's going to rain?"

Tweedledum spread a large umbrella over himself and his brother, and looked up into it. "No, I don't think it is," he said: "at least—not under *here*. Nohow."

"But it may rain *outside*?"

"It may—if it chooses," said Tweedledee: "we've no objection. Contrariwise."

"Selfish things!" thought Alice, and she was just going to say "Good-night" and leave them, when Tweedledum sprang out from under the umbrella, and seized her by the wrist.

"Do you see *that*?" he said, in a voice choking with passion, and his eyes grew large and yellow all in a moment, as he pointed with a trembling finger at a small white thing lying under the tree.

"It's only a rattle," Alice said, after a careful examination of the little white thing. "Not a rattle-*snake,* you know," she added hastily, thinking that he was frightened: "only an old rattle—quite old and broken."

"I knew it was!" cried Tweedledum, beginning to stamp about wildly and tear his hair. "It's spoilt, of course!" Here he looked at Tweedledee, who immediately sat down on the ground, and tried to hide himself under the umbrella.

Alice laid her hand upon his arm, and said in a soothing tone, "You needn't be so angry about an old rattle."

"But it isn't old!" Tweedledum cried, in a greater fury than ever. "It's new, I tell you—I bought it yesterday—my nice NEW RATTLE!" and his voice rose to a perfect scream.

All this time Tweedledee was trying his best to fold up the umbrella, with himself in it: which was such an extraordinary thing to do, that it quite took off Alice's attention from the angry brother. But he couldn't quite succeed, and it ended in his rolling over, bundled up in the umbrella, with only his head out: and there he lay, opening and shutting his mouth and his large eyes—"looking more like a fish than anything else," Alice thought.

"Of course you agree to have a battle?" Tweedledum said in a calmer tone.

"I suppose so," the other sulkily replied, as he crawled out of the umbrella: "only *she* must help us to dress up, you know."

So the two brothers went off hand-in-hand into the wood, and returned in a minute with their arms full of things—such as bolsters, blankets, hearth-rugs, tablecloths, dish-covers, and coal-scuttles. "I hope you're a good hand at pinning and tying strings?" Tweedledum remarked. "Every one of these things has got to go on, somehow or other."

Alice said afterwards she had never seen such a fuss made about anything in all her life—the way those two bustled about—and the quantity of things they put on— and the trouble they gave her in tying strings and fastening buttons—"Really they'll be more like bundles of old clothes than anything else, by the time they're ready!" she said to herself, as she arranged a bolster round the neck of Tweedledee, "to keep his head from being cut off," as he said.

"You know," he added very gravely, "it's one of the most serious things that can possibly happen to one in a battle—to get one's head cut off."

Alice laughed loud: but she managed to turn it into a cough, for fear of hurting his feelings.

"Do I look very pale?" said Tweedledum, coming up to have his helmet tied on. (He *called* it a helmet, though it certainly looked much more like a saucepan.)

"Well—yes—a *little*," Alice replied gently.

"I'm very brave generally," he went on in a low voice: "only to-day I happen to have a headache."

"And *I've* got a toothache!" said Tweedledee, who had overheard the remark. "I'm far worse than you!"

"Then you'd better not fight to-day," said Alice, thinking it a good opportunity to make peace.

"We *must* have a bit of a fight, but I don't care about going on long," said Tweedledum. "What's the time now?"

Tweedledee looked at his watch, and said "Half-past four."

"Let's fight till six, and then have dinner," said Tweedledum.

"Very well," the other said, rather sadly: "and *she* can watch us—only you'd better not come *very* close," he added: "I generally hit every thing I can see—when I get really excited."

"And *I* hit every thing within reach," cried Tweedledum, "whether I can see it or not!"

Alice laughed. "You must hit the *trees* pretty often, I should think," she said.

Tweedledum looked round him with a satisfied smile. "I don't suppose," he said, "there'll be a tree left standing, for ever so far round, by the time we've finished!"

"And all about a rattle!" said Alice, still hoping to make them a *little* ashamed of fighting for such a trifle.

"I shouldn't have minded it so much," said Tweedledum, "if it hadn't been a new one."

"I wish the monstrous crow would come!" thought Alice.

"There's only one sword, you know," Tweedledum said to his brother: "but you can have the umbrella—it's quite as sharp. Only we must begin quick. It's getting as dark as it can."

"And darker," said Tweedledee.

It was getting dark so suddenly that Alice thought there must be a thunderstorm coming on. "What a thick black cloud that is!" she said. "And how fast it comes! Why, I do believe it's got wings!"

"It's the crow!" Tweedledum cried out in a shrill voice of alarm: and the two brothers took to their heels and were out of sight in a moment.

Alice ran a little way into the wood, and stopped under a large tree. "It can never get at me *here*," she thought: "it's far too large to squeeze itself in among the trees. But I wish it wouldn't flap its wings so—it makes quite a hurricane in the wood—here's somebody's shawl being blown away!"

THE MAGIC JACKET

Walter de la Mare

When, that May Day morning, Admiral Rumbold stepped out of his four-wheeled cab at the corner of Pall Mall, he was carrying a small brown-paper parcel. Why he had not told his cabman, who—hunched up on his box—looked older even than his horse, to take him on to exactly where he wanted to go, he hardly knew. He paid the old man his fare; and he added an extra sixpence.

"Thank'ee," he said with a curt nod, then turned to continue on his way. Admiral Rumbold was not exactly a stout man, but in his navy-blue clothes, his neat boots, and brown billycock hat, he looked rather tightly packed. His broad face shone almost as red as a tomato above his white linen collar and blue-and-white spotted silk sailor's knot. He clasped his neat little brown-paper parcel closely under his elbow and at a good round pace proceeded along Pall Mall.

He glanced neither to right nor left of him, but kept his sea-bleached blue eyes fixed steadily ahead. Nor did he show the least sign of recognition when he caught sight of an old friend brandishing a silver-headed cane in his direction from under the hood of a hansom cab. On this particular morning—and the houses and shops looked sparklingly gay in the spring sunshine—Admiral Rumbold wished to be alone. He marched straight on, his eyes fixed, his mouth tight-shut, almost as if he were walking in his sleep.

He turned sharply up St. James's Street, past the saddler's with the jockey caps and jackets behind the glass, past the little bow-windowed snuff-and-tobacco shop, and so into King Street. From King Street he turned off into Duke Street, and then on into Great St. Ann's. After the bustle and traffic now behind him, the quiet sunshine and shadow of Little St. Ann's beyond it was like port after stormy seas.

Now a few paces past the hatter's shop that stood at the corner of Little St. Ann's lay a wide smooth stretch of flat paving stones under a high old brick wall. It was here that a screever or pavement artist had made his pitch; and here in the sunshine Admiral Rumbold came to a halt and looked about him.

The street was still and, at this early hour of the morning, almost deserted. For a while, firm as a rock, he continued so to stand. But having failed to catch a glimpse of what he was after, he began to survey a little vacantly the pictures chalked on the stones at his feet.

The first of them was of a ship with bare masts and lanky spars, tossing on an indigo sea, its waves yeastily crested with spray. Next to this there was a windmill in a gaudy country green, the miller himself standing up like Shem, Ham, and Japhet at the little rounded door above the wide wooden ladder. Next, there was a gaping brace of rainbow-coloured, rather flabby-looking mackerel. Next, a loaf of bread, a cut cheese, and a neat little long-tailed mouse at her supper. And last—and best of all to some tastes—there stood a lonely country mansion among its wintry trees, a wild full moon gleaming down on its walls. Scrawled beneath this picture, in a flowery lettering, was the one word, "HORNTED."

Admiral Rumbold had taken a good long look at these pictures only the evening before. They showed a little livelier in the morning sunshine. Still, he had come back not to have another look at them, but to have a word with the young artist. Few street chalkers, the Admiral had noticed in his walks abroad, are much less than forty. The one he now had in mind could not be more than fourteen. The Admiral had taken a liking to him at first sight, had often watched him at his work, and had dropped many a tuppence into the old cloth cap that usually lay (as if with its mouth wide open) beside the pictures. Now he wished to speak to him.

To an old gentleman with a temper as peppery as the Admiral's it was therefore an unpleasant jar to find that when he wanted the boy he was nowhere to be seen. Besides, he was anxious to get rid of the brown-paper parcel under his arm. He had a dislike to carrying anything at all—even an umbrella so massive that it looked more like a war club. On the other hand he was a man who, having once made up his mind, kept it made up.

He crossed the street, and spent the next few minutes pacing solemnly up and down, glancing ever and again as he did so down the area railings or up at the upper windows of the houses on that side of it, in order to pretend to himself that he was not being kept waiting. And every time he turned smartly on his heel, he glared first up the street, then down the street, and then into the deep-blue, empty sky.

At last he had his reward. Shuffling along close to the railings from out of a neighbouring alley, in shoes that even at this distance looked a good deal more roomy than comfortable, appeared the boy the Admiral was in wait for. A coat that was at least two sizes too large for its present wearer hung down from his bony shoulders. But he had turned the cuffs up over the sleeves, so that his clawlike hands came out free from beneath them.

His odd, almost ugly face was pale and not too clean. His brown hair was lank and tousled. But as the Admiral had noticed before, the skull beneath the hair was nut-shaped and compact, clear over the forehead and wide towards the back. It looked as if it closely fitted something valuable inside it. Besides which, the boy had a pair of eyes in the pinched face looking out from under that skull which once seen were not easily forgotten.

Admiral Rumbold, at sight of him, had slipped in under the carved, shell-shaped porch of one of the neighbouring houses. From here he could see without being seen.

First, the boy glanced into his cap, then took it up, turned it upside down, shook it, and replaced it on the pavement. He then drew a large dingy rag that might once have been the flap of a man's shirt or a woman's petticoat out of his pocket. With both hands he waved this to and fro above his pictures to waft away the dust and straw and soot smuts. He then pushed the rag into his pocket again, and had a steady look at the pictures, as if he had never seen them before and could not make up his mind whether or not to give himself a penny. He then sighed—a sigh that in the morning quietness was clearly audible. At this Admiral Rumbold stepped out of his hiding place, crossed the road, and accosted him.

"Good morning, my boy," was his greeting. "How's business?"

The boy looked up into the round red face of the old gentleman, with its small beak-like nose and sky-blue eyes, and a timid smile passed over his own as he shook his head.

"So, so!" said Admiral Rumbold bluffly. "Nothing much, eh? There's a bit of east in the wind this morning, and perhaps that keeps folk moving. Or perhaps . . . Well, there we are! Had any breakfast? No? Good! I want a word with 'ee. Is there a place handy where we can sit and talk?"

The boy coloured, glanced swiftly from right to left, and told the Admiral of a coffee shop near at hand where he sometimes went himself. Then he looked up at the old Admiral again, became redder than ever, and broke off.

"Full steam ahead, then," said his friend. "And do you lead the way."

The boy buttoned his coat; away they went together; and in a minute or two the pair of them were sitting face to face on two benches between wooden partitions—like the high

pews in old churches—and on either side of a table in an
eating house halfway up the neighbouring alley. The
Admiral asked the boy what he would take. He said a mug
of thick.

At this the Admiral cocked one of his bright blue eyes,
and enquired if he would like anything to eat with it. The
boy hesitated and suggested a doorstep.

"H'm!" said the Admiral, "and anything for a sweet tooth
to follow?"

The boy said he would like a cat's eye. Whereupon
Admiral Rumbold rapped smartly on the table. A man with
greasy black hair, of a dark face, and wearing a rather dingy
apron, appeared from his den behind the shop.

"Good morning," said the Admiral. "Two mugs of thick,
a doorstep, and a cat's eye." And he said the words as if he
had been used to them all his life and knew exactly what
they meant.

The mugs of thick proved to be cocoa; the doorstep, a
slab of bread with a scrimp of butter; and the cat's eye was a
large yellow bun with a burnt raisin stuck in its crown. And
while the two of them sipped their thick, and the boy from
nibbling went on to munching at his doorstep, Admiral
Rumbold explained what he was after.

But first he asked him a little about himself and his
work. He learned that the boy was pretty well alone in the
world. His father, who had been a carriage painter, had
died when he was six. His own business was fair in fine
weather, but it was hard to find a pitch where there were
neither too many passersby nor too few. "And then there's
the bobbies," said the boy. Summer was better than winter,

but up to the last week or two there had been too much rain for any business at all.

"Ay, ay," said the Admiral, looking at him over the thick brim of his mug as he took another sip of cocoa, "a fine-weather trade, I take it." And he asked him what his name was. It was Mike.

"Well now, Mike," said Admiral Rumbold at last, "I've been keeping an eye on you for some little time. I've been *wanting* to keep an eye on someone of your age and looks for a good deal longer. I like your pictures; in fact, I *admire* them. If *I* were to sit down under that wall with every scrap of chalk you've got and do my level best with them, rain or no rain, I warrant my takings wouldn't be fourpence a month. It's the knack you want. And it's the knack, my lad, you have.

"Not, mind you," he went on, "that I know any more about pictures than what I *like*. I leave the rest to them that do. But I've lived a good many years in the world now, and my belief is that every walk in life begins with a steepish bit of hill. When I was a boy—and we're not concerned just now with where *my* walk's led *me*—I had to face mine. And in this parcel here is—well, what helped me in the climbing of it.

"*Here,*" repeated the Admiral and said no more for the moment. For he had brought his square solid hand down on the parcel beside his mug with such a thump that the man in the apron came hurrying up to see what more was wanted.

"I'll have," said the Admiral promptly, "another mug of thick and another couple of doorsteps. And this time put in a slice or two more of beef and bacon by way of cement."

The sandwiches that followed were almost as much meat as bread, and Mike's eyes fairly watered as they were handed over to him.

"In this parcel, as I was saying," continued the Admiral, "is the *story* of what I've been telling you. A yarn, you'll understand. Tell me, can you *read*?" Mike nodded violently; his mouth was full.

"Good!" said the Admiral. "All I want you to do is to read it—it's about a *jacket*—what might be called a slice out of my early days, just as that bacon there may be a slice out of the early days of the pig it came from. There's no hurry—" he glanced at the clock and then at his gold repeater—"it's seventeen and a half minutes past ten. Sit here quietly and read as much of it as you can. When you have finished, come along to me. At eleven sharp I'll be waiting near the pitch.

"Mind ye," he ended as he rose to his feet, "there's no shadow of *must* in that package whatsoever. Nor do I vouch for anything beyond what's written—and I've had it printed out on one of those new-fangled machines so that it can be read plain and easy. Take it quietly; ask for anything you want while I'm away; and in half an hour we meet again."

He put down half-a-crown on the table for the doorsteps, etc., laid his hand an instant on Mike's shoulder, and looked him hard but friendly in the eye. Then he instantly flung open the swing-door of the coffee shop and went out into the street.

To judge from his face, the old gentleman was very well pleased with himself at this moment. He returned to the pictures, and spent the next half-hour, as cautiously as before, in pacing to and fro along the street. Whenever he passed them he paused to look at them, dropped a copper or two into the cap, and went on. At this, some curious passerby would also stop and glance over Mike's gallery. And, maybe, he too would fling in a penny to join the Admiral's—and, maybe, not.

Meanwhile, Mike, left to himself and now the only customer in the coffee shop, took a good long swig of his mug of cocoa and a munch at his sandwich before setting to work on the Admiral's story. And this was what he read:

"Coming down to facts at once, I was born all but seventy years ago, in a town in Shropshire of the name of P——. My father was a grocer—retail. His shop wasn't much to look at from outside, but there was little that his customers wanted in the way of groceries that couldn't be found even then on his shelves.

"My father was a man of about forty when I came into the world. My mother was a good deal younger; and mightily pleased they were to have me. No doubt about that. They christened me Andrew and called me Sandy, there being Scotch blood on my father's side. And if hard work and steady is a shortcut to success, that was my father's way.

"At first, my father and mother were content to live over the shop—three rooms in all, not including one not much bigger than a bandbox, which was called the nursery. When I was six, things were going so well with the business that they decided to let the rooms above the shop, and to move into a small but comfortable, high, and (what they call) semi-detached house, half a mile or so out of the town. We had a good strip of garden there—a few apple and plum trees, some currant and gooseberry bushes, and old country flowers.

"My mother loved that garden, and spent all the time she could spare from the house in it, with me beside her, or digging away at a patch of soil, three yards by one, with scallop shells round the border, which she let me have to do what I pleased with. That was *my* garden. *Sandyland,* she called it. Candytuft, Virginia stock, and sweet william were my own particular crops.

"My mother, I remember, bless her soul, was a great talker. I don't mean by this that she talked too much, or talked to everybody, or never listened. I mean she was a great talker to me, though not so much to my father. What she and I chattered about when we went out shopping in the morning together, or when I used to help her make the beds, would fill a book. Everything under the sun, not to mention the other side of it.

"I don't know what there was about my mother—brown eyes, brown hair, and so on. But hanging up over the pianoforte in what was called our drawing room was a portrait of her as a girl of eighteen or thereabouts which, if I had been any kind of young man with an eye in his head, I should have fallen in love with at first sight. But it wasn't her looks; it was her ways. How to put it I don't know, but she always seemed to be talking as if to somebody over her shoulder as well as to me myself.

"Never—and mine's a pretty long life now—never have I come across anyone with such a loving delight in birds, flowers, trees, clouds, stars, moss, butterflies, and all that. She knew them by heart. You might have thought she'd had a hand in their making. Words aren't my tools, and I must just get things down as straight as I *can*. But that was the way of it. To see her look at a toadstool, with some bright colour to its gills, or peep into a wren's or chaffinch's nest, or stand watching a bevy of long-tailed tits gossiping together for a minute or two in one of our tufted old apple trees on their way to somebody else's, was like—well, I don't know what it wasn't like, except that it was like nothing on earth but my mother. She wasn't any *age* at all. We might have been a couple of brothers or sisters—old cronies, as you might say. We could hardly tell each other apart—except when my father was by.

"Now, I'm not going to say anything against *him*. He died when I was not much more than a quarter of the way up the ladder I was afterwards to set myself to climb. He did his best by me; and if it hadn't been for my own stubborn interference, he might have done better for me than I've done for myself. Can't say; don't *know*. What I wanted was to go my own way, as at last I went. And your own way is nobody else's way. It's a man's self—his *innards,* to speak abruptly—that counts. Not the stripes on his arm, or the cut of his jib, or the cash in his bank, or even what he's *done*.

"But enough of that. The truth is perhaps that being so much alone with my mother, and as contented in her company, at least in those first few years, as a butterfly with a flower, I became a bit of an apron-string child. She did not much care for going out, and she had a mighty small opinion of any young Two-Legs in the street except the one she herself had brought into the world, so I was only allowed to play with any small Tom, Dick, or Harry belonging to our neighbours provided I never went beyond view of her bedroom window. And that's not much of a playground for a healthy young sprat that ought to be learning what the sea looks like.

"Alone with her, and at peace, I wanted nothing else and could chatter away like a grasshopper. Away from her I was usually little better than a tongue-tied numskull, flushing up to the eyebrows at a word from a stranger, and looked too shy and timid to say 'Boh' to a goose—even to the goose in my own looking glass! Well, numskull is as numskull does; and as the old wooden-legged sailor said,

When all you've got is a couple of stump,
There's nowt to do but go clump—clump—clump!

"My father could not see it that way. He began to think I was stupid on purpose. There was not a sharper tradesman in the county, nor a more honest tradesman either, in spite of the 'sharp.' All his wits were at his fingertips. He had a memory like a dictionary. He knew where everything was or ought to be. He could tell a bargain at first wag of its tail and a good customer before he opened his mouth. He lived long enough to make three fine shops of his poky first one—plate-glass windows, plenty of gold paint, three smart vans, and about a dozen glossy-haired assistants in clean white aprons. And he stowed a handsomer show of tea chests, sugar loaves, jam jars, and piccalilli pots behind those windows than any other grocer in the town. I owe him unspeakably more than the little fortune he left me.

"But being what he was, he was impatient with anything else, and particularly with me, his own son. *Now,* I understand it. *Then,* the moment I saw his black hat above the hedge, or heard his key in the lock, I would scuttle away like a frightened rabbit. If we were left alone together, I would sit as glum as a cold plum-duff pudding—without any plums in it! If he asked me a question, every word would fly out of my head, like rooks at a rattle. The mere look of me at such times—fumbling and stammering— made him angry. The more angry he grew the more tongue-tied and lumpish grew I, and that would set my poor mother weeping. And I have never yet met a father who enjoyed being told that he could not understand his own son. Not that he loved me a penny the less; far from it. But love, my boy, is like coal. You can burn it, and warm and comfort yourself with its light and heat. Or you can keep it in a cellar. My father kept his in a cellar—and it was I who helped him stack it up!

"With my mother, as I have said already, everything was different. We would gossip away together for hours. And when she wasn't with me I would talk to myself. I had plenty of books in my bedroom under the roof—books that had belonged to my mother's younger brother who died at sea. And I read like a limpet. When in those days I opened a book that seemed meant for me—travels, voyages, that kind of thing—it was like exploring another world. Fancy tales I never took to—except journeys to the moon, or the middle of the earth, and suchlike—nor could even my mother win me to rhymes.

"Maybe it was all this book stuff and solitude and having nobody to play with that began this odd habit in me of talking to myself when I was alone. And it was this talking to myself that led on to the great discovery. One evening, I remember, I was reading about the supper to which Sir Francis Drake invited the officer on his ship who had been stirring up mutiny against him, and whom he hanged next morning. And as I was listening to myself talking like the officer and putting up as stiff a lip as I could at the prospect of so harsh a breakfast, I suddenly discovered that there was not *one* of me, so to say, but two. I discovered what's called a second self—though of course he must have been there all the time. To make things plain and ship-shape, let us call the first of these two selves, Sandy One; and the second of these two selves, Sandy Two.

"There was first the Sandy One that was my father's son, and stayed at home with his mother in the high, oblong box of a house, standing up high on the hill with its neighbours, all in a row. This was the nervous, timid, stuttering Sandy, the Sandy who did not know where he kept his own tongue, the skulker, the dunderhead whom my father could not make head or tail of. There was next the Sandy who when alone did more or less what he liked and went where he pleased—desert islands, Red Indians, lions and tigers, castaways, cannibals, *bonum omens*—all

that kind of thing. Ay, and the whole world over. *He* pined
for freedom. He wanted to do and dare things. He wanted
to eat his cake and chance the stale crusts afterwards. This
happy-go-lucky, scatter-brained, dare-devil creature boxed
up inside me was Sandy Two. We'll call him, as I say, Sandy
Two; and, Here's good luck to him!—for he needed it!

"Now, do you see, my mother knew something of both
Sandies, though more of One than Two. My father never
so much as dreamt of Two and saw not much more of
One than his worst. And Sandy Two, at his darndest and
daringest, was at present inside my head and kept for
myself and my books alone.

"Now Schooling. . . ."

Mike took a long slow look at this word before going
any further. He was already a little tired of reading. He
wanted to get to the jacket. Still, he had promised the old
gentleman, who seemed to be an old gentleman who expected
his promises to be kept, that he would do his best, and he had
had an *uncommonly* good breakfast. So he swallowed another
gulp of his tepid cocoa, took another huge bite of his
doorstep, and plodded on.

"Now Schooling. Well, I went to school like most boys of
my age. It was what is called a Private School, and the
headmaster's name was Smiles; and his name was not only
where his smiles began but also ended. From the instant my
father led me into his stuffy back room, this Mr. Smiles
took me for a dunce. One glance at my sheepish mottled
face—Sandy One's—was enough for that. And as dunce

he treated me almost until we parted. Dunce was his chief dish with me, from beginning to end—and plenty of cane sauce.

"I hated school. I hated learning. And as I was told to go straight home the moment my lessons were over, I was never much of a favourite with the other boys. They took me for a mollycoddle, and called me Tallow-candy. Which was true of course of Sandy One. And for some little time they never caught sight of Sandy Two. That came later. Still, whenever Sandy One warmed up so much in a scrap as to bring Sandy Two into it, it wasn't the other fellow that left off last!

"Well now, to make a long story short, my father's heart, as I have been saying, was in groceries. And you can take my word for it that there is one thing at least worse than a quick profit on pickles, and that is a dead loss on 'em. His business was growing; he pulled his weight wherever he went; he was soon to be Mayor; and having only one son, he hoped and meant that that son should go into groceries too, and perhaps some day *double* his fortune, keep a carriage, and become *Lord* Mayor. He wanted his son to 'get on,' and what father doesn't?

"So in the old days, just to polish my wits, he would ask me such questions as what raisins are, or where currants come from, or why peel is called candied; and then—with a flicker of his eyelids—who discovered the Macaroni Tree, or how much fresh there is to a pound of salt butter, or where the natives dig up nutmegs, or what is the temperature of Cayenne pepper, or what is the cost of a hogshead of treacle at 2¾*d.* an ounce. The point is, I never even *wanted* to know such things. And worse, I couldn't even laugh at them!

"If my father had asked me what kind of birds you'd be likely to see flitting about in the craters of the moon; or what the war whoop and scalping habits of the Objibwas or the Cherokees were; or how many brothers riding on white asses Abimelech had; I believe Sandy Two would have consented to answer. But Sandy Two (apart from toffee) had no interest whatever in Demerara or Barbados sugar; and Sandy One was no better than a blockhead at any questions whatsoever, except when his mother asked them, or when he was alone.

"One Sunday morning, after I had first said I couldn't answer, and then refused to try to answer, some such questions as these, I looked up and told my father that I hated grocery shops. I said of all shops I hated grocery shops the most. I said I detested school, and that the only thing in the world I wanted was to run away to sea. Then I burst out crying. At this moment my mother came in, so I never got the thrashing I richly deserved.

"But my father must have thought things over; for after that, Dr. Smiles paid very particular attention to the *grocery* side of history, geography, arithmetic, and dictation. Even of French: 'Has your neighbour's gardener the oranges from Jaffa, the tapioca from Brazil, and the chicory for the coffee of his aunt?'—that kind of thing.

"Then one night I overheard my mother and father talking. Sandy Two had come stealing downstairs about half-past nine to see what he could find in the larder. The door of the drawing room was ajar, and I heard my father say: 'He is not only half-witted, but as limp and flabby as a rag doll—and what's more, here's that bladder-of-lard, schoolmaster Smiles, saying exactly the same thing. And yet *you* . . .' At these words Sandy One at once fled back to bed—taking Sandy Two with him. And I awoke next morning remembering what my father had said as distinctly as if it had been tattooed into my skin. For days together after that Sandy Two never so much as showed the tip of his nose in the house.

"Then, one afternoon, on my way home from school, I ventured down a shabby side street, because at the far end of it I had caught the noise of a Punch-and-Judy Show. I could hear the children roaring with laughter, and the squeaking and the thumping and cockadoodle-ing of Mr. Punch. Sandy Two told Sandy One he would like to go and see it. So he went.

"Coming back, we passed a dingy little shop I had never noticed there before, and we stopped to look in at the window. *Marine Store* was printed up in white letters over the green front. There was some queer junk behind that window: old shoes and shawls and old hats, a ship in a bottle, a green glass rolling pin, a telescope that must have belonged to Noah, a ship's compass, a brass cannon, a bed-warmer, a picture made of hummingbirds' feathers—such old curios as they call 'em as that. They looked as if they had been there for centuries—verdigris, mould, fluff, dust. Most of these articles had their prices marked on scraps of paper: '*Grate Bargin, 3s. 6d.*' and so on.

"And hanging up on a nail in a corner of the window and almost out of sight, was a kind of garment I couldn't quite put name to. But a piece of paper was pinned to it, and on that was scrawled the words: *Majick Jacket.* Just that and nothing more. But it was enough. I had already gloated on the telescope and the ship and the brass cannon. But those two words, *Majick Jacket,* fairly took my breath away. They stirred me up as if with a ladle—me myself, Sandy Two, and even Sandy One. At last I could bear the strain no longer.

"I pushed open the crack-paint little door—I can hear even now the jingle of its rusty bell—and in I went. The place smelt like an old cellar. It was as soundless as a vault. For what seemed hours nothing happened, except that I heard a far-away canary singing; then Sandy One began to be alarmed, and I tiptoed off towards the door.

"Just as I was about to whip it open and bolt out into the street again, an old man, with thick magnifying spectacles on his nose and a beard like a goat, came shuffling out of the back parts of the shop and asked me what I wanted.

"I said would he please tell me the price of the brass cannon—though I knew it already. Then I asked to see the ship in the bottle. And then, at last, with hardly any breath left in my body, I managed to point to the jacket.

" 'That,' he said, looking first at it and then at me, 'that's ten shillin'.'

"I got as red as a turkey-cock, coughed, turned about, and opened the door.

" 'I say! I say, Mister!' he called after me. 'What are you running away for? Come back and *see* it. Come back and look at it—*feel* it. No harm in that!' He was already climbing up onto a stool. Then he thrust his head in among the rags and drabs in the window, brought down the jacket, and laid it on the counter. And close-to, like this, it was nothing much, I must say, to look at.

"It was made of some kind of foreign dark Chinese-looking stuff, with a faint wavy pattern on it, and it had flat stone buttons with green crocodiles curled round on them. The braid was frayed at the neck and cuffs. I looked hard at it on the counter, but didn't touch it. Then I blurted out: 'Who made it?'

" 'Made it?' snapped the old man, 'that's a *magic* jacket. That's come from Pekin and Madagascar and Seringapatam and I don't know what, and if once you get inside of it you'll never want to get out again.'

"I swallowed. 'Have *you* ever put it on?' I enquired.

" 'Me?' he almost bellowed at me. 'Me! With all these old slops hanging round! Where should I be if I put 'em all on? Where's the *sale*?'

"Now I wanted that jacket with the crocodiles on the buttons more than anything else past, present, or future in the whole wide world. But I had only two-and-ninepence in my pocket—and that was riches for *me*. To be on the safe side, I told the old man this. He stared at me through his rusting spectacles.

" 'See here!' he said, as if in a violent temper, and whisking out a piece of newspaper from under the counter: 'See here now, snap it!' And he wrapped up the jacket in a flash. 'Give me all you've got, and come back with the rest. There's a summat in your eye, young man, that never went with a cheat.'

"Then I knew that the old man was charging me at least double what he had meant to ask for the jacket. But I gave him my two-and-ninepence all the same, and went out of the shop. Before his door bell had stopped clanging I had pushed the parcel up under my waistcoat and walked off, keeping my stomach in, because I didn't want anybody to ask questions.

"Once safely home, I crept upstairs and slipped the parcel in at the back of a drawer, and for that night there it stayed. I didn't dare to meddle with it, partly for fear of what might happen, but mostly of what might *not*!

"All the next morning I was in torture. I was afraid my mother might find the jacket—and give it away to some tramp for a fern or a pot of geraniums. Every time I thought of it I could scarcely breathe, and that didn't help much in my schoolwork. I was kept in. And when I came home I told my mother I had a headache—which was true—but persuaded her at last to go out and leave me to myself. Then I stole up to my bedroom, shut the door, opened the drawer, and with my heart in my mouth, felt for the parcel. All safe! All *safe*! I took it out, undid the string, opened the paper, and there was the jacket—wavy pattern, crocodile buttons, frayed braid, and all.

"With a last wild look towards the window I took off my own coat and put it on. I put it on. And nothing happened. Nothing whatever. At first blush, I mean. Except that I suddenly noticed that the room was full of sunshine and that a thrush was singing in a pear tree at the bottom of the garden. I noticed it because he sang so clear and shrill, and as though straight at *me*. If you could put sound for sight, it was as if I were listening to him through a telescope. I could see him, too, the speckles on his breast, and his bill opening and shutting—singing like an angel.

"And as I listened I noticed in the sunlight through the window the colours of my faded rose-patterned carpet and an old boot. It sounds silly, but I had never before seen an old boot look like that. I don't want to mince words, and maybe I didn't realise it then, but the fact of the matter is that that old boot on the carpet looked astonishingly *beautiful*—the light on the old leather, the tongue coming out, and the gleam of the metal eyelets. A landshark's word that—*beautiful*—but there you are.

"Well, I was soon a little impatient with all this—a new life seemed to have edged into things, or at least into me. Very peculiar. So, to get back to common sense again, I began Sandy One's *Physical Exercises*. Exercises! Why, it was as though all of a sudden I had become nothing but a twist of wire and catgut. I skipped through those jimminasticals as if I were half out of my senses. Then I tried tricks never so much as dreamt of before—hopping along my bedrail; standing on my head, first on the bedpost, then on my water jug; balancing myself—two hands, then one hand—on the back of a chair. Whatever, within the bounds of reason, or thereabouts, I gave myself to do, I *did*—and with ease. Like the thrush singing. Nothing very much perhaps, but new to *me*! Mind you, I had never been quite the mollie my father thought me. And Sandy Two hadn't been idle, body or wits. But a little confidence, though not too much, is what you want. After a while I began to be a little bit alarmed at the effects of the jacket. I began, so to speak, to suspect my own company!

"So, hot and breathless, I sat down at the table where I always did (or didn't do) my homework, and began my 'composition.' The subject was the Battle of Trafalgar. Before I had finished I had written about fourteen pages on the Battle of Trafalgar! I had described how the *Victory* went to sea, and what Lord Nelson felt like—that last day coming, and why he kept his medals on, and all about Captain Hardy. And I put the weather in, and didn't forget old Froggy Villeneuve either—a gallant sailor and a bad end. When I looked up from page fourteen I could hardly see. It was as if I had come out of the heavenly Jerusalem! And then, almost at that moment, I heard my mother come in down below, and the front door shut.

"I felt like a keg of quicksilver, and yet dead beat. I undressed in less time than a lizard takes to slough its tail, and tumbled into bed, slipping my Chinese jacket in under the bedclothes.

"And no doubt I looked headachy enough when my mother came up to say good night. She felt my forehead; it was burning hot. And she murmured faintly in a very small voice something about castor oil. Even Sandy One could put his foot down when it came to castor oil! But this time I didn't make the least fuss about it. I said, 'Right you are. Warm the glass, mother, and put plenty of lemon juice in.' I swigged it down, and even smacked my lips over it. Then I began to talk—so fast, and with such nonsense mixed up with the sense, that my mother was on the point of calling in the doctor. At that I sobered down again.

"The next day all was well, but I didn't go to school. The next day after that saw me back in my place again, though not in the magic jacket! But I had cut off one of the pale-green crocodile buttons to carry about in my waistcoat pocket for a kind of charm or amulet. I got a caning for the French I hadn't done, and another caning for the arithmetic which I had. Mr. Schoolmaster Smiles himself read my *Essay on the Battle of Trafalger* then and there. He hauled me out again before the class, and asked me what help I had had. I said none. He glared at me: 'Are you positively sure, sir? Not even in the spelling?'

"I said, 'No sir; none, sir.' What was queer, he believed me.

"Still, he had talked to me once or twice about the sea and the Navy. And I too had asked him questions, because while I was wrapped up in the thought of them, I wasn't so frightened of him. Besides, on looking back, I don't believe he really cottoned to groceries much more than I did. Anyhow, he gave me full marks and a bit over for my Trafalgar, but warned me another time I mustn't 'spread' myself out like that.

"I went home feeling like a turkey-cock, marched straight upstairs, sat down at my open window, and—put on the jacket again. But I had hardly got my arms into the sleeves when I heard my mother calling me. I hustled on my own jacket over the top of the other—which was not difficult, because my Chinese one was a very tight fit, especially at the armpits—and met her on the landing. She was as white as a sheet and could scarcely speak. She said my father wanted to see me at once, and that he had a friend with him, a Mr. Turner.

" 'And, oh, my dear,' she implored me, 'do try and answer your father's questions. Just *listen*, Sandy. Then perhaps you'll hear. And speak up to Mr. Turner, too, if he speaks to you. Think it's *me*. Don't be frightened; don't be *sulky*. Nobody can eat you. Fancy it's only just you and me talking. For my sake, Sandy.'

"I said, 'Right, Mother!' and slid from top to bottom down the banisters of the three flights of stairs almost before she had stirred foot to follow me. At the dining room door I pulled myself together and went in.

"My father was sitting on the other side of the fireless hearth, talking to a stranger. I liked the look of this stranger. He was short and broad; his face was burnt with the sun; he had a fringe of reddish hair round his head, and wore thick-soled shoes. 'Here he is,' said my father to the stranger, then turned to me. 'This gentleman is Mr. Turner, Andrew. If you want to know anything about the sea, he'll tell you.' I put out my hand.

" 'I hear you've no stomach for dry goods,' said Mr. Turner, staring at me, but in a friendly fashion. 'Have a hankering after salt water, eh?'

" 'Yes,' I said, 'the Navy.' Out of the corner of my eye I saw my father start at this. He had never before heard me answer so direct a question without stammering or flushing or just goggling like a red herring with its mouth open.

" 'And what do you know about the sea?' said Mr. Turner, looking at me steadily. 'It's pretty deep!'

"I looked back at him no less steadily. I liked him more and more, and thought I would try him with a few tidbits out of my fourteen pages on the Battle of Trafalgar. There was a queer silence when I had finished. And I realised that my mother had at that moment stolen away after listening at the door. As for my father, he sat in his chair dumb with amazement. He shut his eyes for an instant and then began to explain that I was not perhaps so backward in some things as in others. But, apart from mere book-learning, did Mr. Turner think that I had the framework, the grit, the *health* for a life in the open? 'You see, his mother . . .'

" 'He looks a bit pasty,' said Mr. Turner, still quietly grinning at me. 'But you can't always tell by the skin. What about those biceps, young man?'

"I put out my arm, and he gripped it hard above the elbow, not noticing, perhaps, that I had two jackets on. And he said, 'Pretty good. Do they drill you much at school? Or is it nothing but book-learning?' I nodded, and said, 'Yes; and things at home, too.'

" 'What do you do at home?' says he.

"Now all this time I had been feeling like a bottle of ginger beer before the cork pops out. So when he gave the word, so to speak, I upped with my heels and pretty nearly *trotted* across the room on the palms of my hands.

" 'Bravo,' said Mr. Turner. 'Try that on the table.'

"It was a circular, solid, old-fashioned mahogany table, made when Queen Victoria was a girl, and I circumnavigated it on my fingers and thumbs as nimbly as a cat. But now my blood was up. To give me room, a couple of tumblers, a bottle of water, and a decanter of whisky had been pushed into the middle of the table. Balancing myself on one hand, I poured out with the other a noggin of the water—for I couldn't quite venture on the whisky—into one of the tumblers, and singing out, *'Nelson, forever!'* drank it off. Then, spluttering and half-choking, I got down from the table, and at last looked at my father.

"He was so pale as to be all but green. He looked as if he was seasick. He said, 'Has your mother ever seen you do such things as that?' I shook my head. But Mr. Turner was laughing. What's more, he hadn't finished with me yet.

" 'Have you got such a thing as a stout piece of rope, William—say a dozen fathom?' he asked my father. There were few things my father was *not* possessor of. We went out into the garden, and as neat as ninepence Mr. Turner flung a bight of the rope over one of the upper branches of a fine shady sycamore that grew so close to the house that its leaves in summer actually brushed against its windows.

" 'Try that, young man,' said my father's friend, Mr. Turner, when he had made it fast.

"Well, whether it was due to the devil in Sandy Two or only to the workings of the magic jacket, I don't know, but I shinned up that unknotted rope like a monkey up a palm tree. And when I reached the top, I edged along on my stomach till I was almost at the end of the bough. Then at arms' length I began to dandle on it—up and down, up and down, like a monkey on elastic. When it had given me enough swing and impetus—what's called *momentum*—I let go—and landed as pat as a pea-shooter through the open window onto the landing, the sill of which was some twelve feet from the ground.

"When I came down into the garden again, my father and Mr. Turner were having a close, earnest talk together, under the sycamore. My father looked at me as if I had just come back from the Andaman Islands.

"I said, 'Was that all right, Daddy?'

"But he made no answer; only patted me on the shoulder, turning his head away. And from that moment, and forever after, we were the best of friends, my father and I; though he never had the ghost of a notion of what had caused Sandy Two—whom, mind you, he had never noticed before—to sprout like that!

"But then, that's how things go. And—to cut a long story short—by hook and by crook, by twisting and turning—chiefly my father's—which would take too long to put down in black and white, I won free of groceries at last for good and all. And the next spring I went to sea for a trial voyage. And after *that,* though it was pretty hard going—well, I got into the Navy.

"And now, here I am, for good and all on land again. Not much short of being an old man, but still, thank God, hale and hearty, and able and willing, I hope, to do a fellow creature a good turn at need. And this, my lad, is where *you* come in.

"The fact of the matter is, I had watched you scrabbling away with your chalks at your pitch in Little St. Ann's a good many days before you knew it. And I came to two conclusions. First, that your pictures are proof that you can do good work. And second, that you could do much better.

187

What I feel is you keep *yourself* back, do you see? It's the old story of Sandy One and Sandy Two. You haven't the confidence, the go, the guts (in a word), to forge clean ahead, *your* way.

"That's what I say. I see you setting to work in the morning like a young cockatrice, but presently you begin to waver, you become slack and dispirited. The least little mishap—a broken chalk, some oaf *walking* over the pictures, even a cloud floating up over the sun—shakes your nerve. At such times you don't seem to be sure even of what you want to do, let alone how to do it. You niggle at a picture first one way, then another, and at the end give it up in despair, the zest gone, and the fancy gone, and the spirit—what I call the innards—gone too. And when any stranger speaks to you, or drops a copper in your cap, you flush up, droop, go limp and dumb, and look as if butter wouldn't melt in your mouth.

"Now first, my boy, don't mind what I am saying. It is for your *sake*. I wouldn't be taking the trouble except only and solely in the hope and wish of doing you a small service. And remember this, I've been through it all before you—and may, when the end comes, again. I've known what it is to feel my bones melt in my body, to tremble like a jelly, my face like a plaster mask and my skull as empty as a hulk on a sandbank. In two words, I know of old what it's like to be *Sandy One*. So, you see, it's because I'm morally certain there's a Sandy *Two* in *you*—and maybe one beyond anything I can conjecture—that I'm writing this now.

"I like the cut of your jib, and the way you stick to things in spite of all dispiritment and the dumps. I had my eye on him when you marked the mug (for good, I hope) of that suety butcher's boy the other day who spat on your Old Boney. I want to give you a hand *in your own line,* and see no better way of doing it than by just lending you my old Pekin jacket for a bit. Now what do you think about that?

"Maybe it won't work. Maybe its magic's gone. Maybe I imagine as much as I remember about it. But I can say *this*—the last time I squeezed into it before the toughest engagement I ever came out of alive, I reckon it blew up the enemy's ship at least two hours before she'd have gone to the bottom in the usual way. Mind you, I haven't *often* used it. When I was your age, an hour or two of it tired me out for half the next week. A day or two of it might take a complete month to recover from. Besides, if you look at the matter by and large, and fair and square, you can see it wouldn't do. In the long run we have to trust to what we have in us that's constant and natural, so to speak, and work like a slave at that. It's only in tight corners we need a little extra fire and frenzy. *Then* maybe Dame Fortune will see fit to lend a helping hand.

"So all I say is, give the jacket a trial. There is almost room for two of you in it—so if you don't want it to be noticeable, put it on under your own coat, and see how things go. And last, remember this, my boy: whatever happens, I shall still be keeping an eye on you. As my dear mother used to say, 'There may be more than one way

189

home, Sandy—but it's trudging does it.' And here's good luck; God bless you; and *Finis.*"

It was the last page of Admiral Rumbold's "yarn." Mike turned it over, looked at the back, coughed, and drank down what was left of his cold cocoa. He wiped his mouth with the back of his hand and looked up as he did so at the round yellow face of the clock that hung on the wall at the further end of the shop. At that very moment, it seemed, it had begun to tick. The long hand stood at two minutes before the hour. The old gentleman must be expecting him now—this very minute! Had he meant him to open the parcel and put on the jacket inside it there and then? His face flushed, then paled—he couldn't make up his mind. His head was in a whirl; his heart thumping under his ribs; he broke out hot and damp all over.

While he was still debating what he should do, he noticed that the man who had brought him the food—with his long tallow-coloured face and pale grey eyes—was steadily though vacantly watching him. Mike got up in haste, pushed the remnants of his last doorstep of beef and bacon into his pocket, hastily snatched up the Admiral's manuscript and brown-paper parcel, and left the eating house.

Before actually turning the corner which would bring him in sight of his pitch, he peeped round to see if the old gentleman was anywhere to be seen. He certainly was. At this actual moment he was walking away from Mike— square, compact shoulders, brown billycock hat, and firm rolling tread. When once more he returned to the pictures he paused, looked them over one by one, dropped something into the cap, and continued on his way. In less than a minute or so he was back again, had taken another look, and once more paid his fee.

It appeared as if Admiral Rumbold had been so engaged ever since he had left Mike in the coffee shop; and there could be no doubt he had by this means attracted passersby to follow his example and look at the pictures. Many, it is true, just glanced and passed on; but a few paid their coppers. The old gentleman was now approaching the street corner where Mike was in hiding, so Mike stepped out a little shamefacedly and met him there and then.

"Aha!" cried Admiral Rumbold. "So there you are! Good! And sharp to time. Did you finish it? Good! Have you got it on?"

Mike went red, then white. He said: "I have read it, every page, sir, but the jacket's still in the paper, because—"

"Be dashed to 'Because'!" cried the Admiral. "Come a pace or two down that alley yonder. We'll soon put that right."

So they went off together into the shelter of an alley nearby, above which the green leaves of a plane tree showed over the glass-bottled wall; and Mike, having taken off his own old loose long coat, slipped into the Chinese jacket as easily as an eel, and then back into his own again on top of it. Admiral Rumbold, having crushed up the brown paper into a ball, tied the string round it, and lightly flung it over the wall. "Good luck to it!" said he.

"Now," he added, and looked at Mike—then paused. The boy stood motionless, as though he were frozen, yet he was trembling. His lips were moving. He seemed to be trying to say something for which he could not find the words. When at last he lifted his face and looked up, the old Admiral was astonished at the black-blue of his eyes in his pale face. It was the dark, dazzling blue of deep seas. The Admiral could not for the life of him remember where he had seen eyes resembling them. They were unlike the eyes of boy or man or child or woman, and yet *somewhere* he had seen their like. Mike was smiling.

"The green crocodiles, sir," he said, fingering one of the buttons. "Most of them are not much bigger than ha'pennies, but you can feel all the horny parts, and even the eyes stickin' out of their heads."

"Ay, ay," said the Admiral. "That's Chinese work. That's how *they* work—at least in times gone by. But how do you feel, how do you *feel,* my lad?"

Mike gazed up an instant at his old friend; then his glance roved on and upwards towards the pale-green pentagonal plane leaves above his head and the patch of blue and sunny sky beyond. A smart northwest breeze was blowing, and a mountainous cloud was moving up into the heights of noonday.

"I'd like," he answered huskily, "to get back to the pitchers, sir."

"Ay, ay!" cried the Admiral. And again, "Ay, ay! Back we go." So the two of them set off together.

And though to all outward appearance the old gentleman, whose face was all but as red as a pimento, was as cool as a cucumber when he came stumping along beside his young acquaintance, his excitement was intense. It was

Mike who had now taken the lead. The Admiral was merely following in his wake. The boy seemed utterly changed, made over again. There was a look to him even as he walked that was as lively as a peal of bells. It was as if *his* bright and burning sun had suddenly shone out between clouds as cold as granite, lighting up the heavens. What was to happen next?

First, Mike took up his cap, and with not even a glance at what was inside it, emptied its contents into his coat pocket. He then paced slowly on from one picture to the next, until he had scrutinised the complete seven. From the pocket with the remains of the "doorstep" in it he then drew out his capacious strip of rag and hurried off to a dribbling water standard with a leopard's head on the spout about twenty-five yards away. There he wetted his rag through and through. He came back to his pictures, and in a few moments had completely rubbed every one of them out. No more than the faintest blur of pink and yellow was left to show that the paving stones had ever lost their usual grey, and in three minutes that was dowsed out too.

When he had finished this destruction, and the warm morning air had dried the stones again, he knelt down and set to work. He seemed to have forgotten the old Admiral, the Chinese jacket, everything that had happened that morning. He seemed to be wholly unaware of the passersby, the dappling sunbeams, the clatter and stir of the street, and even who and where and what he was. Skinny and engrossed, he squatted on his hams there, huddled up under the wall, and *worked.*

Admiral Rumbold, as he watched him, became almost alarmed at the rapidity with which things were taking shape on the blank paving stones. As if by magic and before his very eyes there had loomed into view a full-rigged ship, swimming buoyant as a swan on the blue of its waters, its masts tapering up into the heavens, its sails bellying like drifts of snow; while from its portholes pushed the metal mouths of such dogs as he himself had often heard bark, and seldom to no purpose.

It was not so much the resemblance of this picture to a real ship on a real sea under a real sky that drew out of his mouth a grunted, "Begad, begad!" but something in the look of the thing, some spirit living and lovely and everlasting behind it all, to which he could not have given name, but which reminded him of the eyes that had looked up at him a few minutes before under the plane leaves in the alley after their first intense glance at the crocodile buttons. Yes, and reminded him too of an evening long ago when he had made the circuit of his mother's mahogany dining table on little more of his anatomy than his thumbs.

By this time a few other wayfarers had begun to collect and to watch the young street artist at his work. It did not seem to matter that he had forgotten to put back his cap in its customary place, that in fact it was on his head, for, oddly enough, when these idlers turned away, though every single one of them seemed to marvel at the quickness and skill of the boy, yet they all seemed *anxious* to be gone, and nobody gave him a ha'penny.

Admiral Rumbold could stand the strain no longer. He firmly placed a half-crown beside the little heap of coloured chalks, coughed loudly, paused an instant, and then, seeing that Mike had not noticed him, stole off and left him to his work.

The worst of the Admiral's anxieties were over. There could be no doubt in the world that the magic jacket had lost not one whit of its powers since first he had slipped into it himself all but sixty years ago. The only thing that troubled him was that not a single farthing had been bestowed on the young artist in the last quarter of an hour. Nevertheless, he thought he knew why.

"They're scared!" he muttered to himself. "They don't know what to make of it. They see it's a marvel and a miracle—and beyond 'em. They don't like the smell of it. They think it's dangerous. They just watch and wonder and sneak away. Well, my dear Rumbold, why *not*? Have patience. Never mind that. Wait and see!"

He loaded himself up with coppers the next morning, and returned very early to the narrow terrace behind Great St. Ann's. The night before had been rainless; only the lightest of dews had fallen. It had been windless, too, and there was a moon; so that the row of pictures which Mike had left unfinished on the pavement must have faintly bloomed under her beams that whole night long, and now were as fresh as they were at the first making of them. Admiral Rumbold had sallied out at this unusual hour to steal a glance at them alone; but Mike had been up before him.

There he was—on his knees once more—deaf and blind it seemed to everything in the world outside him, and intent only on his pictures. His old friend didn't interrupt him, but left him to himself, and went off to get some breakfast at his club. When he returned the boy had vanished for the time being. Five pictures out of the customary seven were now complete.

The Admiral stared and stared at them, part in astonishment, part in inexpressible delight, and part in the utmost dismay. Two of them—the ship, "The Old Victery," and the new "Hornted"—were more vivid and astonishing things than (with French chalks and paving stones) he had thought even possible. The rest, he felt uneasily, were beyond his comprehension. He could hardly make head or tail of them.

One was called "Peepul at Sunset." It reminded him of Shadrach, Meshech, and Abed-nego walking in the midst of the burning fiery furnace. Another was called "The Blind Man"; it showed a chair, a table with a bowl of flowers, and a dish of fruit on it. There was an open window, too. It seemed to shimmer and glow and blaze like precious stones. But to the Admiral's eye the chair was all clumped and crooked, and the flowers looked queer— half human. He had never in all his born days seen a picture of a chair like that. Besides, there was not even a sign of a human being, let alone a blind man, to be seen! He stirred, coughed softly. He sighed, and glanced into the ragged cap. It was now a quarter to ten; the cap contained a French penny, a British ha'penny, and a three-penny bit with a hole in it. The Admiral lugged out of his pocket a handful of coppers, and added them to what was there. Off and on throughout the day he kept an eye on the young street artist. Of two things he was at last certain:

196

first, that Mike was still wearing the jacket; and next, that he had made (apart from his donations) practically no profit. For you cannot pick up coloured chalks in the gutter, or patch the knees of your old breeches with the empty air! The boy could hardly have taken an independent sixpence.

Admiral Rumbold began to be a little anxious as he thought this dark fact over, but decided not to interfere. Next day he knocked fairly early at the door of a lodging house nearly opposite Mike's pitch.

"Good morning," he said, as soon as it was opened. "I'd like, if you please, to have the window again. Is it free?"

"Certainly, sir," said the woman who had answered his knock. "I'm glad you enjoy the view, sir. It's a pity there's so much wall."

"It's not the bricks, ma'am, but the people," replied the Admiral, as he followed her up a flight of stairs into a room which immediately overlooked the street.

There—behind the Brussels curtains at the window, and seated on a rather lumpy armchair—the Admiral spent most of his morning, watching all that went on in the street below, but especially the boy. And once more he came to two conclusions: first, that Mike was *not* now wearing the jacket, and next that he was making less money even than the day before. *Life* seemed to be gone out of him. He sat hunched up beside his chalks and his empty cap—his bony face as grey as ashes. He hardly dared even raise his eyes when anybody paused to examine his pictures. Now and again, however, he would glance anxiously up and down the street as if in search of somebody.

197

"He's looking for me," muttered the Admiral to himself. "He wants to return the jacket. God bless *me*! Still, steady does it; steady does it."

He returned to his window in the early afternoon. The boy looked even more miserable and dejected than ever, but nonetheless he had begun to tinker a bit at his picture, "The Old Victery." On this occasion the Admiral had brought field glasses with him. With these he could now watch his young friend at work so closely as almost to fancy he could hear him breathe. Indeed, he could see even a round-headed ant making its way along the crack between two paving stones; and the tiny bits of chalk resembled coloured rocks.

Mike laboured on, now rubbing out, now chalking in, and the Admiral could follow every tint and line and stroke. At last—though by no means as if he were satisfied—the boy stood up and examined what he had done. At sight of it he seemed to droop and shrink. And no wonder. The Admiral almost wept aloud. The thing was ruined. There was the ship, there the sea, and there the sky; but where the lovely light and airiness, the romance, the wonder? Where the *picture*?

Admiral Rumbold was at his wits' end. The day was drawing on. He began to think that his intended kindness had ruined the boy for good and all. He sat back in his chair absolutely at a loss what to do next. One thing was certain. He must go soon and have a word with the boy— hearten and liven him up. He must give him a good square meal, put some "beef" into him, and—perhaps— take the jacket back. It had been little but a deceit and a failure. He must take the jacket back, then think things over.

He leant forward to rise from his chair, and as he did so cast a last desperate glance at the opposite side of the street. Then he paused. Fine weather was still in the heavens. The first colours of evening were beginning to stretch across London's skies—shafts of primrose, melted gold, and faint crimson lighting up the walls of the houses, flooding the streets with light. And Mike was no longer alone. He was still squatting tailor-fashion under his wall and as motionless as if he had been carved out of ebony, but a pace or so away stood an odd-looking old gentleman in a sort of long curry-coloured ulster. This old gentleman had a beard and wore a high conical black felt hat with a wide rim to it. An umbrella, less neat but more formidable in appearance even than the Admiral's, was tucked under his arm.

He was not merely looking at, he was intent on, "lost" in the pictures. He stooped over them each in turn, spending at least two or three minutes over every one, except "The Old Victery," at which he just glanced and went on.

When he found himself at the end of the row, he turned back and examined them all over again. Admiral Rumbold watched these proceedings with bated breath. The old man in the ulster had now turned to Mike, who at once scrambled to his feet, leaving his chalks, his cap, and a small newspaper parcel on the pavement. The two of them in the clear-coloured evening light were soon talking together almost as if they were father and son. They were talking about the pictures, too; for every now and again Mike's new acquaintance, bent almost double, would point with the stump of his umbrella at one of them, tracing out a line, or hovering over a patch of colour. At the same time, his beard turned over his shoulder towards Mike, he would seem to be praising, or criticising, or explaining, or asking questions. Once, indeed, he stooped, caught up a piece of chalk, and himself drew a few lines on the pavement as if to show the boy exactly what he meant. "So!" the Admiral heard him end, brushing his fingers.

There could be no doubt this eccentric old gentleman in the wide black hat was interested not only in the pictures but also in Mike. He looked as if in his excitement he might go on talking till midnight. But no; at this very moment he seemed to be making some kind of proposal to the boy. He had put his hand on his shoulder as if in encouragement. Mike hesitated, then cast a long look into the sky, as if to consult the weather. After that his mind seemed to be made up. He hastily took up his cap, his chalks, and his parcel, and the two of them set off down Little St. Ann's together.

At this Admiral Rumbold paused no longer. He seized his hard billycock hat, his field glasses, and his malacca cane, and clattered down the stairs out into the street. Keeping well behind them, he followed Mike and the old gentleman out of Little St. Ann's into Ashley Court, and so across into Jermyn Street. At this corner, so intent was he in his pursuit, that he barely escaped being run over by a two-horse grocery van.

Mike and the old gentleman were now so clearly in sight that the Admiral had time to pause and address a policeman.

"Good evening, constable," he said. "I want you to tell me if by any chance you happen to know the *name* of that old gentleman in the hat yonder, walking with that lad there?"

The policeman fixed his eyes on the pair.

"Well, sir, to tell you the truth, sir," he said at last, "I've *seen* him somewhere though I couldn't say rightly just where. I've even been told who he *is*. But bless me, if I can lay tongue to the name of him. I wish I could, sir. He looks as if it might be worthwhile." Admiral Rumbold thanked the policeman and hastened on.

At the moment when he once more came within sight of the two of them a long-haired youngish young man in a dark, loose cape or cloak had but just met and passed them by. This young man was also wearing a black, wide-brimmed hat. As soon as politeness permitted, he not only stopped dead, but stood intently watching the pair until Admiral Rumbold himself had come up with him. The Admiral glanced him over.

"You will excuse me, sir," he said, "but if I am not mistaken, you are as much interested in that old gentleman yonder as I am myself. A most impressive figure! Could you oblige me with his *name?*"

"His *name,* sir!" exclaimed the young man. "Gracious heavens! Why, that's old B———. That's 'old B. in a Bonnet!'—the crankiest, craziest old creature in the British Isles. But make no mistake, sir. What that old boy doesn't know about pictures and painting isn't worth a tallow candle. He's a Master. Wait till he's dead, that's all. Then the whole world will be wagging with him."

"You don't say *so!*" shouted the Admiral. "A *Master! Painting!*—eh? I am very greatly obliged to 'ee—very greatly obliged. And you think if he's taken a fancy to that lad there—*sees* promise in him, I mean—well—that the lad's in luck's way?"

" 'Think?' " replied the young man. "Bless your heart, sir, I *know.*"

The Admiral detained him no longer. He saluted him and passed on. He could say no more. He was satisfied. All was well. The magic jacket, then, had *not* played him false; Mike's "steepish bit of hill" was well begun. He found himself at the further end of Jermyn Street, and in the traffic of the Haymarket. The old man in the ulster had disappeared. But no, there he was—old B.—some little distance down on the opposite side of the street, and at the window of a printseller's shop. He was talking to the boy at his side—pointing, gesticulating, his bushy beard wagging. And Mike was listening, gazing in, entranced. Admiral Rumbold turned on his heel. He had never professed to know much about pictures. Then why should he now suddenly feel downcast and depressed? He was tired, too, and extremely thirsty. It was almost as if he missed his jacket.

Props for Faith

Ursula Hegi

When our housekeeper told me she didn't think the midwife was Renate's real mother, I wondered if my best friend's parents were gypsies, those dark-haired women and men who, every July, set up the carnival on the Burgdorf fairgrounds and, with brown, ring-covered hands, took the groschen I'd saved for rides on the ferris wheel and pink clouds of cotton candy. *Gypsies.* That would explain Renate's dark, frizzy hair, her quick, black eyes. But gypsies moved rapidly, while my friend walked with a limp, her feet in patent-leather shoes, her fragile ankles hidden under white knee socks that never stayed up.

Besides—gypsies were known to steal babies.

Not give them away.

After swearing me to secrecy, Frau Brocker told me, "I figure her real parents were too poor to keep her. Too many other children already." She'd just come back from her

weekly visit to the beauty parlor and she smelled of hair
spray. "Instead of paying the midwife, they must have given
her the baby."

The midwife was a blond, heavy widow whose husband
had been killed during the war on the Russian front. She'd
delivered me and most of the kids I knew. Her name was
Hilde Eberhardt, and she lived with her older son, Adi, and
Renate in a white stucco house two blocks from school. No
one had seen her pregnant with Renate, not even Trudi
Montag. Twelve years before the midwife had left town one
Thursday, and the following day she had returned with a
dark-haired infant girl, claiming it was hers. By then her
son had lived half of his five years without a father.

Renate didn't come to our school until the end of second
grade, and we became best friends right away. Nearly two
years earlier, she'd been taken to the Theresienheim with
pneumonia. On the day she was to be released, she fell
when she climbed out of bed, caved in on herself like a
puppet whose strings had been cut. The nuns suspected
polio and rushed her to St. Lukas hospital in Düsseldorf
where the doctors confirmed the diagnosis and kept her for
over a year, probing her legs with needles. Though she was
eventually cured, her left leg was shorter than the other.
Thinner. Both legs were pale with large pores.

Whenever Renate took me to her house, the midwife
examined the soles of our shoes and followed us around
with a mop, catching any speck of dust that dropped from
our skirts and settled on her glossy parquet floor. Yet, when
I got ready to leave, she'd say, "Come back, Hanna. Any
time."

Their yard, too, was orderly: a lush lawn without dande-
lions; window boxes with forget-me-nots and geraniums;
a trimmed hedge of purple lilacs. The one imperfection
was a pear tree that produced abundant blossoms but only
yielded hard little pears with brown spots.

With his blond hair and blue eyes, Renate's brother, Adi,
didn't look anything like Renate. His full name was Adolf,
but no one called him that. Quite a few boys in the grades
above us were called Adolf—a name that had been popular
for babies born in the early war years—but we had no
Adolfs in our class or in the younger grades. The name
Adolf Hitler was never mentioned in our history classes.
Our teachers dealt in detail with the old Greeks and
Romans; we'd slowly wind our way up to Attila the Hun, to
Henry the Eighth who had six wives, to Kaiser Wilhelm,
to the First World War; from there we'd slide right back to
the old Greeks and Romans.

In gym class Renate was always the last in line—awkward,
hesitant, everything about her slow except for those dark
eyes that seemed to move right through me. But I hardly
thought about the polio or her leg until Sybille Immers, the
butcher's daughter, called Renate a gimp one day as we left
school. I leapt at Sybille, who was taller and heavier than I,
kicking her shins; she raked her fingernails across my face
and tore at my hair. When Frau Buttgereit, our music
teacher, pulled us apart, her green hat with the pheasant
feather fell into a puddle.

I still can't understand what I did less than a week later
when Renate didn't want to come out and play.

"Why not?" I shouted, standing outside her bedroom window.

She leaned on the windowsill with both hands. "Because," she shouted back.

"Because why?"

"Because Sybille is coming over."

The scratches on my face still itched, and there she was, looking for a new best friend. Something hot and sad and mean rose inside me and, before I could stop myself, I yelled, "Even the gypsies didn't want to keep a gimp like you!"

Her arms tight against her body, Renate stood motionless. Her face turned red, then ashen.

I stared at her, horrified by what I had said. My throat ached, and when I tried to talk, I couldn't bring out one word.

"Hanna!" the side door slammed and the midwife ran toward me, her eyes filled with tears. "Don't you ever come back here," she shouted and raised one hand. "You hear me, Hanna?"

"But I didn't mean it," I cried out as I ran from her.

"I didn't mean it," I told Renate in school the next day, but she said she wasn't allowed to play with me anymore and walked away.

Her limp seemed worse than ever before, and I felt as if I had caused it. If only I could take back the words. During recess, she stood alone in the schoolyard, eating an apple. My hands in the pockets of my pleated skirt, I leaned against the fence close by, feeling hollow despite the cheese sandwich I'd just eaten. If only she'd call me something real bad, something worse than gimp. Even if she said that my parents had found me at the dump, or that my mother should have thrown me away as a baby because I was too ugly to keep—I pushed my fists deeper into my pockets, jammed back my elbows into the diamond-shaped holes in the fence.

After school I waited for her outside the building. "Do you want to buy some licorice?"

She shook her head.

"I still have my allowance."

"I'm not hungry."

"We could ride bikes."

"I have to go home." She crossed the street.

I followed her on the opposite sidewalk. Mist hung low above the streets and garden walls, yet left the trees and houses untouched. Frau Weskopp passed us on her bicycle, her black coat flapping around her. I could tell she was on her way to the cemetery because a watering can dangled from her handlebar. When Renate reached her front door, she turned around as if she wanted to make sure I was close by before she slipped inside.

I left my books at our house and walked toward the river. The streets were damp; it had rained nearly every day that April. When I got close to the Tegerns' house, the architect's seven German shepherds threw themselves against the chain-link fence, barking. The skin above their gums was drawn back, and their teeth glistened. Though Renate and I always ran past the fence, I made myself stop on the sidewalk, close enough to smell the wet fur and see the strings of saliva on the dogs' tongues. I snarled back at them. The hair on their backs rose as they scrambled across each other, trying to climb up the fence, barking and howling at me.

"Cowards," I hissed, wishing Renate could see me. I raised my hands, curled my fingers into claws. "Cowards."

A curtain shifted in the window above the solarium and Frau Tegern knocked against the glass, motioning me away as if afraid for me or, perhaps, herself. I gave the dogs one final ferocious growl and turned my back to them.

Along the river the mist was thicker, and the water looked brown-green, darker than the meadow where a herd of sheep grazed. I heard the tearing of grass blades as their teeth closed around them. The shapes of poplars and willows were blurred. Above the water line the rocks were gray and damp, the upper ones splotched with a white crust.

Frau Brocker used to bring Rolf and me to the river when we were small. While she smoked one of her Gauloises, Rolf and I searched for scraps of paper and dry leaves, packing them into the crevices between the stones before setting a match to them.

I sat on a boulder and dug my sneakers into the heaps of pebbles around me. Maybe if I gave Renate a present . . . I could let her have my radio. Or any of the dolls in my room. I didn't play with them anyhow. But neither did Renate. I picked up a pebble, tried to flit it across the waves; it sank without rising once. Perhaps we could switch bicycles. She liked mine better than hers. It had even been touched by holy water at the pastor's last blessing of the vehicles and didn't have any rust on it.

If I were Renate, the thing I'd want most in the world—
it was so simple—her leg, of course, her left leg, to have it
grow and fill out like the other one. I thought of my
Oma's* healer—not even a saint—who'd touched her leg
and dissolved a blood clot in the artery below her knee.
Oma had told me it was as much her belief in the healing
as the healing itself that had saved her leg from having to
be amputated. Miracles happened that way. Even without
saints. As long as you believed in them. I bent to search for
a flat, round pebble and found a white one with amber
veins. After spitting on it for luck, I skipped it across the
water. It sprang up in wide arcs four, five . . . a total of
eight times.

That evening I looked around our cellar for an empty
bottle. Our housekeeper stored things there which she
said she might use some day: cardboard boxes with old
magazines and brochures, empty bottles and jars, a four-
liter pot with a hole in the bottom, a stained lampshade,
even the tin tub I'd been bathed in until I was two. Most
of the bottles were too large, but finally I found an empty
vinegar bottle behind the washing machine.

I soaked off the label, rinsed the inside, and hid it in my
room until Wednesday morning when St. Martin's Church
was empty because mass was held at the chapel. The bottle
in my knapsack, I sneaked into the side door of the church
early before school. In the morning light the blond wood of

---

* **Oma.** German for "Grandma."

the pews gleamed as if someone had rubbed it with oil. The stale scent of incense made it hard to breathe. Though I knew Herr Pastor Beier was at the chapel two kilometers away, I kept glancing toward the purple curtains of the confessional.

Marble steps with a red runner led to the altar, which was built of solid black marble. Centered between two silver bowls with tulips stood five candles thicker than Renate's legs. From *The Last Supper* mural above the altar, the dark eyes of Jesus and the apostles traced my movements. I'd heard enough stories about church robbers to know the wrath of God could strike at any moment and leave me dead on the floor. As I walked toward the back of the church to the basin of holy water, the white veins in the marble floor reached for my feet like the nets of a fisherman.

Quickly I submerged my vinegar bottle in the cold water. Silver bubbles rose to the surface as the bottle filled—much too slowly. On the wide balcony above me, I felt the silent weight of the organ pipes.

"You want to come to my house?" I whispered to Renate as I followed her out of school that afternoon.

She shook her head and kept walking, tilting to the left with each step, her white knee socks bunched around her ankles.

"It's about a surprise."

She glanced at me sideways. "What is it?"

"I can't tell." My knapsack over one arm, I continued walking next to her. "I have to show it to you."

210

"Why?"

"Because. It's a secret."

"What if I don't want it?"

"You will. I swear."

She stopped. "Is it a harmonica?"

"Better."

"Better than a kitten?"

"Much better."

"Better than—"

"The best thing that could happen to you," I promised.

She still had some doubt in her eyes as we took the steps down to our cellar. I thought of the nights my mother and grandmother had hidden there with neighbors while the wail of sirens pierced the dark. The war had ended a year before Renate and I were born. Several kids in our school had lost their fathers at the Russian front. Adults never mentioned the war unless we asked about it, and then they fled into vague sentences about a dark period for Germany. "Nobody wants to relive those years," they'd say gravely. My mother was the only one who answered some of our questions and told us about the terror of air raids, the hunger and cold everyone had suffered.

"Sit over there." I pointed to the crates next to the apple shelves. Every fall my father and I filled those crates with apples we'd picked at an orchard in Krefeld. Afterward we'd wrap the apples in newspaper and lay them on the shelves. It was my job to rotate them every two weeks, sorting out the rotten ones, so the others would last through the winter.

Renate sat on the crate closest to the door. The wall at the far end of the cellar was still black, right up to the two high windows that were blind with layers of coal dust and cobwebs. Until the oil furnace had been installed two years before, I used to help my father stack coal briquets to within a hand's width of the window.

I picked up the other crate and moved it in front of Renate. "You have to take off your left shoe and sock."

"Why?" She straightened her shoulders.

"Because. It's part of it. You'll see." I took the bottle from my knapsack.

Renate pulled her bare foot from the cement floor. "It's cold."

I sat down on the crate across from her. "Let me have your leg." When she hesitated, I whispered, "I've figured out a way to make it all right—your leg, I mean—heal it."

She swallowed hard. "How?"

"It'll be like your other leg."

She drew her lower lip between her teeth, but then she raised her left leg and, carefully, laid her bare foot on my knees. It was a pale foot, a thin foot with toenails longer than mine, a foot that felt warm and sweaty as I put one hand around it to keep her from yanking it back.

With my teeth I uncorked the bottle. "All you need to do is close your eyes and believe it will work."

"What's in there?" Renate stared at me.

"Holy water." I poured some of it into my palm. It felt cold and smelled musty.

"Wait." She reached into her mouth with her right forefinger and thumb and took out a pink wad of chewing gum. After sticking it on the side of her crate, she closed

212

her eyes and raised her face as though about to receive communion.

I rubbed the holy water up and down Renate's calf, between her toes, along the arch of her foot. Light filtered in uneven splotches from the dust-smeared light bulb above us. I've always had an enormous capacity to believe. Stories, miracles, lies—with the right details, I can be convinced of the authenticity of nearly anything, even *Hasenbrot,* rabbit bread, which my father brought me many evenings when he returned from working on people's teeth. Handing me half a sandwich wrapped in oil-stained brown paper, he'd tell me that on his way home he'd seen a *Hase,* a rabbit, by the side of the road, carrying this package—he'd motion to the sandwich—between its front paws. He leapt from his car to catch it, but the *Hase* ran off with the bundle; my father followed it across the brook and chased it along Schreberstrasse until the *Hase* finally dropped the package next to the brook and disappeared. The bundle was about to slide into the water when my father saw it.

Every time my father chased the *Hase* through a different area, and every time there was that one breath-catching moment when the bundle was almost lost all over again because a car nearly ran over it or a dog tried to tear it from his hands. I'd unfold the brown paper with something bordering on reverence. Though the bread was always a bit stale, the meat limp, and the cheese soggy, I've never tasted anything as delicious as my father's *Hasenbrot.*

And it was with that kind of faith that I dribbled holy water over Renate's foot and leg. I kneaded it into the crescent-shaped callus at her heel, into the bony disk of her knee. Her teeth had released her lower lip, and she breathed evenly.

Already I felt a difference in her leg: the skin seemed warmer and didn't look as pale anymore. With each day her leg would stretch itself, grow fuller, stronger. It would be able to keep up with the other leg when she pedaled her bike. She'd play hopscotch. Tag.

"You can look now."

Renate blinked, staring at me, then at her leg.

"See?" I bent over her leg, my heart fast.

Cautiously she probed her ankle with her fingertips, then her calf. "I think so."

"It's already begun to change."

"Are you sure?"

"Absolutely."

"Should we do it again tomorrow? To make double sure?"

"No," I said, instinctively knowing the difference between a miracle and a treatment. "All you need to do is believe it worked."

She raised her leg from my knees. "It feels different."

"See?"

"What do we do with the rest of the holy water?"

I hadn't even thought of that. The bottle was still half full. It didn't feel right to pour it out or leave it here in the basement.

"We could drink it," Renate suggested.

I felt as if the eyes of the apostles were watching me as I raised the bottle to my lips, swallowed, and gave it to Renate who drank and handed it back to me. It tasted the

214

way damp stones smell and within an hour I had stomach cramps, punishment, no doubt, for stealing holy water, a sin I didn't dare confess.

Over the next weeks I watched for signs of change in Renate's left leg. I pictured the pores closing, the skin losing its chalky color, the calf filling out.

"Does it feel different?" I'd ask her, and she'd nod and say, "I think so."

The end of April we took our bicycles to the annual blessing of vehicles on the Burgdorf fairgrounds where Herr Pastor Beier sprinkled holy water on cars, trucks, tractors, motor scooters, and bikes to keep them in good condition and out of accidents. Renate still couldn't keep up with me as we rode back to her house. By then the midwife had accepted my apology and welcomed me back into her house, all the time cleaning up behind us.

In July Renate and I picked purple clover blossoms on the fairgrounds and watched the gypsies set up their tents and booths. I found myself staring at their faces, afraid to discover resemblances between Renate and them, relieved when I didn't. We rode the merry-go-round, ate white sausages with mustard, threw Ping-Pong balls through wooden loops. The biggest tent had been set up for the circus, and Renate's mother took Adi and us to the Saturday performance. We applauded when five fat clowns tumbled out of a tiny car, when the animal tamer stuck his head inside the lion's mouth, and when the elephants circled the arena, their trunks holding the tails of the elephants ahead of them.

During intermission Adi bought us candied apples, and when we returned to our seats, the lights dimmed. It turned dark inside the tent, and the voices faded into whispers, then silence. High above us a slow shimmer began to spread. It came from a woman with black hair who stood on the tightrope in a short golden dress. I felt Renate's hand on my arm; her fingers were dry, warm. The woman's arms and legs shimmered as she set one foot in front of the other and crossed the wide gap.

If there were nets that day in the circus, Renate and I didn't see them. We believed the woman was safe. It had to do with faith. We had proven that to ourselves that afternoon in the cellar when the holy water had worked after all, not healing Renate's leg but the rift between us. Some acts of faith, I believe, have the power to grant us something infinitely wiser than what we imagine. We all have our props for faith, and the shakier the faith, the more props we need. But sometimes the faith is strong enough so that an old vinegar bottle with holy water and a crate next to the apple shelves will do.

CHARACTERS IN "THE JUNGLE BOOKS"

(pronunciations based on the Hindi)

AKELA [A-*kay*-la] The leader of the Seeonee wolf pack when Mowgli comes to the jungle as a baby; also called the Lone Wolf.

BAGHEERA [Bag-eera, pronounced like an "era" in history] The black panther who, for the price of a newly slain bull, bought the infant Mowgli's acceptance into the Seeonee wolf pack.

BALOO [*Bar*-loo] The wise, old brown bear who teaches wolf cubs the Law of the Jungle. He, along with Bagheera, spoke in favor of admitting Mowgli into the Seeonee wolf pack.

BANDAR-LOG [Bunder-logue] The Monkey-people.

BULDEO [*Bul*-doo] The village hunter who led the movement to cast Mowgli out.

CHIL [Cheel] The kite, a bird of prey and a scavenger.

DHOLE [Dole] A fierce, wild red dog of India.

FERAO [Feer-*ow*] The scarlet woodpecker.

HATHI [Huttee] The elephant, also called the Silent One.

KAA [Kar, with a sort of gasp in it] The rock python who befriends Mowgli; head of the Middle Jungle.

MESSUA [*Mes*-war] Mowgli's human mother.

MOWGLI ["Mow" rhymes with "cow"] The boy who grows up as a wolf in the jungles of India.

MYSA [*Mi*-sar] The wild buffalo.

NATHOO [Nut-too] Messua's name for Mowgli.

RAKSHA [*Ruck*-sher] "The Demon"—Mowgli's wolf mother. Her children, including Grey Brother, are known as the Four.

SEEONEE [See-*own*-y] The name of Mowgli's wolf pack.

SHERE KHAN [Sheer Karn] The tiger who hunted Mowgli and whom Mowgli eventually slays; also called Lungri, the Lame One.

TABAQUI [Ta-*bar*-kee] The jackal, a follower of Shere Khan; also called Dish-licker.

LETTING IN THE JUNGLE

Rudyard Kipling

You will remember, if you have read the tales in the first *Jungle Book,* that after Mowgli had pinned Shere Khan's hide to the Council Rock, he told as many as were left of the Seeonee Pack that henceforward he would hunt in the jungle alone; and the four children of Mother and Father Wolf said that they would hunt with him. But it is not easy to change all one's life at once—particularly in the jungle. The first thing Mowgli did, when the disorderly pack had slunk off, was to go to the home-cave, and sleep for a day and a night. Then he told Mother Wolf and Father Wolf as much as they could understand of his adventures among men. And when he made the morning sun flicker up and down the blade of his skinning-knife—the same he had skinned Shere Khan with—they said he had learnt something. Then Akela and Grey Brother had to explain their share of the great buffalo-drive in the ravine,* and Baloo toiled up the hill to hear all about it, and Bagheera scratched himself all over with pure delight at the way in which Mowgli had managed his war.

It was long after sunrise, but no one dreamed of going to sleep, and from time to time, Mother Wolf would throw up her head, and sniff a deep snuff of satisfaction as the wind brought her the smell of the tiger-skin on the Council Rock.

"But for Akela and Grey Brother here," Mowgli said, at the end, "I could have done nothing. Oh, Mother, Mother! If thou hadst seen the blue herd-bulls pour down the ravine, or hurry through the gates when the man pack flung stones at me!"

"I am glad I did not see that last," said Mother Wolf, stiffly. "It is not *my* custom to suffer my cubs to be driven to and fro like jackals! *I* would have taken a price from the man pack, but I would have spared the woman who gave thee the milk. Yes, I would have spared her alone."

"Peace, peace, Raksha!" said Father Wolf, lazily. "Our frog has come back again—so wise that his own father must lick his feet. And what is a cut, more or less, on the head? Leave Man alone." Baloo and Bagheera both echoed: "Leave Man alone."

Mowgli, his head on Mother Wolf's side, smiled contentedly, and said that, for his own part, he never wished

---

* In "Tiger-Tiger!" Mowgli kills his enemy Shere Khan by trapping
  the tiger in a ravine through which he drives a herd of buffalo.
  When the villagers, fearing this "magic," throw stones at Mowgli,
  he angrily turns the herd and drives it through the village.

to see, or hear, or smell Man again.

"But what," said Akela, cocking one ear, "but what if men do not leave thee alone, Little Brother?"

"We be *five*," said Grey Brother, looking round at the company, and snapping his jaws on the last word.

"We also might attend to that hunting," said Bagheera, with a little *switch-switch* of his tail, looking at Baloo. "But why think of Man now, Akela?"

"For this reason," the Lone Wolf answered. "When that yellow thief's hide was hung up on the rock, I went back along our trail to the village, stepping in my tracks, turning aside, and lying down, to make a mixed trail in case any should follow us. But when I had fouled the trail so that I myself hardly knew it again, Mang the Bat came hawking between the trees, and hung up above me. Said Mang: 'The village of the man pack, where they cast out the man-cub, hums like a hornet's nest.' "

"It was a big stone that I threw," chuckled Mowgli, who had often amused himself by throwing ripe pawpaws into a hornet's nest, and racing to the nearest pool before the hornets caught him.

"I asked of Mang what he had seen. He said that the Red Flower blossomed at the gate of the village, and men sat about it carrying guns. Now *I* know, for I have good cause"—Akela looked here at the old dry scars on his flank and side—"that men do not carry guns for pleasure. Presently, Little Brother, a man with a gun follows our trail—if, indeed, he be not already on it."

"But why should he? Men have cast me out. What more do they need?" said Mowgli angrily.

"Thou art a man, Little Brother," Akela returned. "It is not for us, the Free Hunters, to tell thee what thy brethren do, or why."

He had just time to snatch up his paw as the skinning-knife cut deep into the ground below. Mowgli struck quicker than an average human eye could follow, but Akela was a wolf, and even a dog, who is very far removed from the wild wolf, his ancestor, can be waked out of deep sleep by a cart-wheel touching his flank, and can spring away unharmed before that wheel comes on.

"Another time," Mowgli said, quietly, returning the knife to its sheath, "speak of the man pack and of Mowgli in *two* breaths—not one."

"*Phff!* That is a sharp tooth," said Akela, snuffing at the blade's cut in the earth, "but living with the man pack has spoiled thine eye, Little Brother. I could have killed buck while thou was striking."

Bagheera sprang to his feet, thrust up his head as far as he could, sniffed, and stiffened through every curve in his body. Grey Brother followed his example quickly, keeping a little to his left to get the wind that was blowing from the right, while Akela bounded fifty yards upwind, and, half-crouching, stiffened too. Mowgli looked on enviously. He could smell things as very few human beings could, but he had never reached the hair-trigger-like sensitiveness of a jungle nose, and his three months in the smoky village had put him back sadly. However, he dampened his finger, rubbed it on his nose, and stood erect to catch the upper scent, which, though the faintest, is the truest.

"Man!" Akela growled, dropping on his haunches.

"Buldeo!" said Mowgli, sitting down. "He follows our trail, and yonder is the sunlight on his gun. Look!"

It was no more than a splash of sunlight, for a fraction of a second, on the brass clamps of the old Tower musket, but nothing in the jungle winks with just that flash, except when the clouds race over the sky. Then a piece of mica, or a little pool, or even a highly polished leaf will flash like a heliograph. But that day was cloudless and still.

"I knew men would follow," said Akela, triumphantly. "Not for nothing have I led the pack!"

Mowgli's four wolves said nothing, but ran down hill on their bellies, melting into the thorn and underbrush.

"Whither go ye, and without word?" Mowgli called.

"*Hsh!* We roll his skull here before midday!" Grey Brother answered.

"Back! Back and wait! Man does not eat Man!" Mowgli shrieked.

"Who was a wolf but now? Who drove the knife at me for thinking he might be a man?" said Akela, as the Four turned back sullenly and dropped to heel.

"Am I to give reason for all I choose to do?" said Mowgli, furiously.

"That is Man! There speaks Man!" Bagheera muttered under his whiskers. "Even so did men talk round the king's cages at Oodeypore. We of the jungle know that Man is wisest of all. If we trusted our ears we should know that of all things he is most foolish." Raising his voice, he added: "The man-cub is right in this. Men hunt in packs. To kill

223

one, unless we know what the others will do, is bad hunting. Come, let us see what this man means towards us."

"We will not come," Grey Brother growled. "Hunt alone, Little Brother. *We* know our own minds! The skull would have been ready to bring by now."

Mowgli had been looking from one to the other of his friends, his chest heaving and his eyes full of tears. He strode forward, and, dropping on one knee, said: "Do I not know my mind? Look at me!"

They looked uneasily, and when their eyes wandered, he called them back again and again, till their hair stood up all over their bodies, and they trembled in every limb, while Mowgli stared and stared.

"Now," said he, "of us five, which is leader?"

"Thou art leader, Little Brother," said Grey Brother, and he licked Mowgli's foot.

"Follow, then," said Mowgli, and the Four followed at his heels with their tails between their legs.

"This comes of living with the man pack," said Bagheera, slipping down after them. "There is more in the jungle now than Jungle Law, Baloo."

The old bear said nothing, but he thought many things.

Mowgli cut across noiselessly through the jungle, at right angles to Buldeo's path, till, parting the undergrowth, he saw the old man, his musket on his shoulder, running up the two-day-old trail at a dog-trot.

You will remember that Mowgli had left the village with the heavy weight of Shere Khan's raw hide on his shoulders, while Akela and Grey Brother trotted behind, so that the trail was very clearly marked. Presently Buldeo came to where Akela, as you know, had gone back and mixed it all up. Then he sat down, and coughed and grunted, and made little casts round and about into the jungle to pick it up again, and all the time he could have thrown a stone over those who were watching him. No one can be so silent as a wolf when he does not care to be heard, and Mowgli, though the wolves thought he moved very clumsily, could come and go like a shadow. They ringed the old man as a school of porpoises ring a steamer at full speed, and as they ringed him they talked unconcernedly, for their speech began below the lowest end of the scale that untaught human beings can hear. (The other end is bounded by the high squeak of Mang the Bat, which very many people cannot catch at all. From that note all the bird and bat and insect talk takes on.)

"This is better than any kill," said Grey Brother, as Buldeo stooped and peered and puffed. "He looks like a lost pig in the jungles by the river. What does he say?" Buldeo was muttering savagely.

Mowgli translated. "He says that packs of wolves must have danced round me. He says that he never saw such a trail in his life. He says he is tired."

"He will be rested before he picks it up again," said Bagheera coolly, as he slipped round a tree-trunk, in the game of blind-man's-buff that they were playing. "*Now,* what does the lean thing do?"

"Eat or blow smoke out of his mouth. Men always play with their mouths," said Mowgli. And the silent trailers saw the old man fill and light, and puff at a water-pipe, and they took good note of the smell of the tobacco, so as to be sure of Buldeo in the darkest night, if necessary.

Then a little knot of charcoal-burners came down the path, and naturally halted to speak to Buldeo, whose fame as a hunter reached for at least twenty miles round. They all sat down and smoked, and Bagheera and the others came up and watched while Buldeo began to tell the story of Mowgli the Devil-Child from one end to another, with additions and inventions. How he himself had really killed Shere Khan; and how Mowgli had turned himself into a wolf, and fought with him all the afternoon, and changed into a boy again and bewitched Buldeo's rifle, so that the bullet turned the corner, when he pointed it at Mowgli, and killed one of Buldeo's own buffaloes; and how the village, knowing him to be the bravest hunter in Seeonee, had sent him out to kill this devil-child. But meantime the village had got hold of Messua and her husband, who were undoubtedly the father and mother of this devil-child, and had barricaded them in their own hut, and presently would torture them to make them confess they were witch and wizard, and then they would be burned to death.

"When?" said the charcoal-burners, because they would very much like to be present at the ceremony.

Buldeo said that nothing would be done till he returned, because the village wished him to kill the jungle boy first. After that they would dispose of Messua and her husband, and divide their land and buffaloes among the village. Messua's husband had some remarkably fine buffaloes, too. It was an excellent thing to destroy wizards, Buldeo thought, and people who entertained wolf-children out of the jungle were clearly the worst kind of witches.

But, said the charcoal-burners, what would happen if the English heard of it? The English, they had been told, were a perfectly mad people, who would not let honest farmers kill witches in peace.

Why, said Buldeo, the head-man of the village would report that Messua and her husband had died of snakebite. That was all arranged, and the only thing now was to kill the wolf-child. They did not happen to have seen anything of such a creature?

The charcoal-burners looked round cautiously, and thanked their stars they had not, but they had no doubt that so brave a man as Buldeo would find him if anyone could. The sun was getting rather low, and they had an idea that they would push on to Buldeo's village and see the wicked witch. Buldeo said that, though it was his duty to kill the devil-child he could not think of letting a party of unarmed men go through the jungle, which might reveal the wolf-demon at any minute, without his escort. He, therefore, would accompany them, and if the sorcerer's child appeared—well, he would show them how the best hunter in Seeonee dealt with such things. The Brahmin, he said, had given him a charm against the creature that made everything perfectly safe.

"What says he? What says he? What says he?" the wolves repeated every few minutes. And Mowgli translated until he came to the witch part of the story, which was a little beyond him, and then he said that the man and woman who had been so kind to him were trapped.

"Do men trap men?" said Grey Brother.

"So he says. I cannot understand the talk. They are all mad together. What have Messua and her man to do with me that they should be put in a trap, and what is all this talk about the Red Flower? I must look to this. Whatever they would do to Messua they will not do till Buldeo returns. And so—" Mowgli thought hard with his fingers playing round the haft of his skinning-knife, while Buldeo and the charcoal-burners went off very valiantly in single file.

"I go hot-foot back to the man pack," Mowgli said at last.

"And those?" said Grey Brother, looking hungrily after the brown backs of the charcoal-burners.

"Sing them home," said Mowgli with a grin. "I do not wish them to be at the village gate till it is dark. Can ye hold them?"

Grey Brother bared his white teeth in contempt. "We can head them round and round in circles like tethered goats—if I know Man."

"That I do not need. Sing to them a little lest they be lonely on the road, and, Grey Brother, the song need not be of the sweetest. Go with them, Bagheera, and help make that song. When night is laid down, meet me by the village—Grey Brother knows the place."

"It is no light hunting to track for a man-cub. When shall I sleep?" said Bagheera, yawning, though his eyes showed he was delighted with the amusement. "Me to sing to naked men! But let us try."

He lowered his head so that the sound would travel, and cried a long, long "Good hunting"—a midnight call in the afternoon, which was quite awful enough to begin with.

Mowgli heard it rumble, and rise, and fall, and die off in a creepy sort of whine behind him, and laughed to himself as he ran through the jungle. He could see the charcoal-burners huddled in a knot, old Buldeo's gun-barrel waving, like a banana-leaf, to every point of the compass at once. Then Grey Brother gave the *Ya-la-hi! Yalaha!* call for the buck-driving, when the pack drives the nilghai, the big blue cow, before them, and it seemed to come from the very ends of the earth, nearer, and nearer, and nearer, till it ended in a shriek snapped off short. The other three answered, till even Mowgli could have vowed that the full pack was in full cry, and then they all broke into the magnificent morning-song in the jungle, with every turn, and flourish, and grace-note, that a deep-mouthed wolf of the pack knows. This is a rough rendering of the song, but you must imagine what it sounds like when it breaks the afternoon hush of the jungle:

> One moment past our bodies cast
>   No shadow on the plain;
> Now clear and black they stride our track,
>   And we run home again.
> In morning-hush, each rock and bush
>   Stands hard, and high, and raw:
> Then give the call: *"Good rest to all*
>   *That keep the Jungle Law!"*
>
> Now horn and pelt our peoples melt
>   In covert to abide;
> Now crouched and still, to cave and hill
>   Our jungle barons glide.
> Now, stark and plain, Man's oxen strain,
>   That draw the new-yoked plough;
> Now stripped and dread the dawn is red
>   Above the lit *talao.*

229

Ho! Get to lair! The sun's aflare
 Behind the breathing grass:
And creaking through the young bamboo
 The warning whispers pass.
By day made strange, the woods we range
 With blinking eyes we scan;
While down the skies the wild duck cries:
 "The day—the day to Man!"

The dew is dried that drenched our hide,
 Or washed about our way;
And where we drank, the puddled bank
 Is crisping into clay.
The traitor dark gives up each mark
 Of stretched or hooded claw;
Then hear the call: *"Good rest to all
 That keep the Jungle Law!"*

But no translation can give the effect of it, or the yelping scorn the four threw into every word of it, as they heard the trees crash when the men hastily climbed up into the branches, and Buldeo began repeating incantations and charms. Then they lay down and slept, for like all who live by their own exertions, they were of a methodical cast of mind, and no one can work well without sleep.

Meantime, Mowgli was putting the miles behind him, nine to the hour, swinging on, delighted to find himself so fit after all his cramped months among men. The one idea in his head was to get Messua and her husband out of the trap, whatever it was, for he had a natural mistrust of traps. Later on, he promised himself, he would begin to pay his debts to the village at large.

It was at twilight when he saw the well-remembered

grazing-grounds, and the *dhâk*-tree where Grey Brother had waited for him on the morning that he killed Shere Khan. Angry as he was at the whole breed and community of Man, something jumped up in his throat and made him catch his breath when he looked at the village roofs. He noticed that everyone had come in from the fields unusually early, and that, instead of getting to their evening cooking, they gathered in a crowd under the village tree, and chattered, and shouted.

"Men must always be making traps for men, or they are not content," said Mowgli. "Two nights ago it was Mowgli—but that night seems many rains old. To-night it is Messua and her man. To-morrow, and for very many nights after, it will be Mowgli's turn again."

He crept along outside the wall till he came to Messua's hut, and looked through the window into the room. There lay Messua, gagged, and bound hand and foot, breathing hard, and groaning. Her husband was tied to the gaily painted bedstead. The door of the hut that opened into the street was shut fast, and three or four people were sitting with their backs to it.

Mowgli knew the manners and customs of the villagers very fairly. He argued that so long as they could eat, and talk, and smoke, they would not do anything else, but as soon as they had fed they would begin to be dangerous. Buldeo would be coming in before long, and if his escort had done its duty Buldeo would have a very interesting tale to tell. So he went in through the window, and, stooping over the man and the woman, cut their thongs, pulling out the gags, and looked round the hut for some milk.

Messua was half wild with pain and fear (she had been beaten and stoned all the morning), and Mowgli put his hand over her mouth just in time to stop a scream. Her husband was only bewildered and angry, and sat picking dust and things out of his torn beard.

"I knew—I knew he would come," Messua sobbed at last. "Now do I *know* that he is my son." And she caught Mowgli to her heart. Up to that time Mowgli had been perfectly steady, but here he began to tremble all over, and that surprised him immensely.

"Why are these thongs? Why have they tied thee?" he asked, after a pause.

"To be put to the death for making a son of thee—what else?" said the man, sullenly. "Look! I bleed."

Messua said nothing, but it was at *her* wounds that Mowgli looked, and they heard him grit his teeth when he saw the blood.

"Whose work is this?" said he. "There is a price to pay."

"The work of all the village. I was too rich. I had too many cattle. *Therefore* she and I are witches, because we gave thee shelter."

"I do not understand. Let Messua tell the tale."

"I gave thee milk, Nathoo. Dost thou remember?" Messua said, timidly. "Because thou wast my son, whom the tiger took, and because I loved thee very dearly. They said that I was thy mother, the mother of a devil, and therefore worthy of death."

"And what is a devil?" said Mowgli. "Death I have seen."

The man looked up gloomily under his eyebrows, but Messua laughed. "See!" she said to her husband. "I knew—I said that he was no sorcerer! He is my son—my son!"

"Son or sorcerer, what good will that do us?" the man answered. "We be as dead already."

"Yonder is the road through the jungle." Mowgli pointed through the window. "Your hands and feet are free. Go now."

"We do not know the jungle, my son, as—as thou knowest," Messua began. "I do not think that I could walk far."

"And the men and women would be upon our backs and drag us here again," said the husband.

"Hm!" said Mowgli, and he tickled the palm of his hand with the tip of his skinning-knife. "I have no wish to do harm to anyone of this village—yet. But I do not think they will stay thee. In a little while they will have much to think upon. Ah!" He lifted his head and listened to shouting and trampling outside. "So they have let Buldeo come home at last?"

"He was sent out this morning to kill thee," Messua cried. "Didst thou meet him?"

"Yes—we—I met him. He has a tale to tell, and while he is talking it there is time to do much. But first I will learn what they mean. Think where ye would go, and tell me when I come back."

He bounded through the window and ran along again outside the wall of the village till he came within earshot of the crowd round the peepul-tree. Buldeo was lying on the ground, coughing and groaning, and everyone was asking him questions. His hair had fallen about his shoulders; his hands and legs were skinned from climbing up trees, and he could hardly speak, but he felt the importance of his position keenly. From time to time he said something about devils and singing devils, and magic enchantment, just to give the crowd a taste of what was coming. Then he called for water.

"*Bah!*" said Mowgli. "Chatter—chatter! Talk, talk! Men are blood-brothers of the *Bandar-log.* Now he must wash his mouth with water; now he must blow smoke; and when all that is done he has still his story to tell. They are very wise people—men. They will leave no one to guard Messua till their ears are stuffed with Buldeo's tales. And—I grow as lazy as they!"

He shook himself and glided back to the hut. Just as he was at the window he felt a touch on his foot.

"Mother," said he, for he knew that tongue well, "what dost *thou* here?"

"I heard my children singing through the woods, and I followed the one I loved best. Little Frog, I have a desire to see that woman who gave thee milk," said Mother Wolf, all wet with the dew.

"They have bound and mean to kill her. I have cut those ties, and she goes with her man through the jungle."

"I also will follow. I am old, but not yet toothless." Mother Wolf reared herself up on end, and looked through the window into the dark of the hut.

In a minute she dropped noiselessly, and all she said was: "I gave thee thy first milk, but Bagheera speaks truth: Man goes to Man at the last."

"Maybe," said Mowgli, with a very unpleasant look on

his face, "but to-night I am very far from that trail. Wait here, but do not let her see."

"*Thou* wast never afraid of *me*, little frog," said Mother Wolf, backing into the high grass, and blotting herself out, as she knew how.

"And now," said Mowgli, cheerfully, as he swung into the hut again, "they are all sitting round Buldeo, who is saying that which did not happen. When his talk is finished, they say they will assuredly come here with the Red—with fire and burn you both. And then?"

"I have spoken to my man," said Messua. "Khanhiwara is thirty miles from here, but at Khanhiwara we may find the English—"

"And what pack are they?" said Mowgli.

"I do not know. They be white, and it is said that they govern all the land, and do not suffer people to burn or beat each other without witnesses. If we can get thither to-night we live. Otherwise we die."

"Live then. No man passes the gates to-night. But what does *he* do?" Messua's husband was on his hands and knees digging up the earth in one corner of the hut.

"It is his little money," said Messua. "We can take nothing else."

"Ah, yes. The stuff that passes from hand to hand and never grows warmer. Do they need it outside this place also?" said Mowgli.

The man stared angrily. "He is a fool, and no devil," he muttered. "With the money I can buy a horse. We are too bruised to walk far, and the village will follow us in an hour."

"I say they will *not* follow till I choose, but a horse is well thought of, for Messua is tired." Her husband stood up and knotted the last of the rupees into his waistcloth. Mowgli helped Messua through the window, and the cool night air revived her, but the jungle in the starlight looked very dark and terrible.

"Ye know the trail to Khanhiwara?" Mowgli whispered. They nodded.

"Good. Remember, now, not to be afraid. And there is no need to go quickly. Only—only there may be some small singing in the jungle behind you and before."

"Think you we would have risked a night in the jungle through anything less than the fear of burning? It is better to be killed by beasts than by men," said Messua's husband. But Messua looked at Mowgli and smiled.

"I say," Mowgli went on, just as though he were Baloo repeating an old Jungle Law for the hundredth time to an inattentive cub, "I say that not a tooth in the jungle is bared against you, not a foot in the jungle is lifted against you. Neither man nor beast shall stay you till you come within eyeshot of Khanhiwara. There will be a watch about you." He turned quickly to Messua, saying: "*He* does not believe, but thou wilt believe?"

"Aye, surely, my son. Man, ghost, or wolf of the jungle, I believe."

"*He* will be afraid when he hears my people singing. Thou wilt know and understand. Go now, and slowly, for there is no need of any haste. The gates are shut."

Messua flung herself sobbing at Mowgli's feet, but he lifted her very quickly with a shiver. Then she hung about his neck and called him every name of blessing she could think of, but her husband looked enviously across his fields, and said: "*If* we reach Khanhiwara, and I get the ear of the English, I will bring such a lawsuit against the Brahmin and old Buldeo and the others as shall eat this village to the bone. They shall pay me twice over for my crops untilled and my buffaloes unfed. I will have a great justice."

Mowgli laughed. "I do not know what justice is, but—come thou back next rains and see what is left."

They went off towards the jungle, and Mother Wolf leaped from her place of hiding.

"Follow!" said Mowgli. "And look to it that all the jungle knows these two are safe. Give tongue a little. I would call Bagheera."

The long, low howl rose and fell, and Mowgli saw Messua's husband flinch and turn, half minded to run back to the hut.

"Go on," Mowgli shouted, cheerfully. "I said there might be singing. That call will follow up to Khanhiwara. It is the favour of the jungle."

Messua urged her husband forward, and the darkness shut down on them and Mother Wolf as Bagheera rose up almost under Mowgli's feet, trembling with delight of the night that drives the Jungle-People wild.

"I am ashamed of thy brethren," he said, purring.

"What? Did they not sing sweetly to Buldeo?" said Mowgli.

"Too well! Too well! They made even *me* forget my pride, and, by the broken lock that freed me, I went singing through the jungle as though I were out wooing in the spring! Didst thou not hear us?"

"I had other game afoot. Ask Buldeo if he liked the song. But where are the Four? I do not wish one of the man pack to leave the gates to-night."

"What need of the Four, then?" said Bagheera, shifting from foot to foot, his eyes ablaze, and purring louder than ever. "I can hold them, Little Brother. Is it killing at last? The singing and the sight of the men climbing up the trees have made me very ready. Who is Man that we should care for him—the naked brown digger, the hairless and tooth-less, the eater of earth? I have followed him all day—at noon—in the white sunlight. I herded him as the wolves herd buck. I am Bagheera! Bagheera! Bagheera! As I dance with my shadow so I danced with those men. Look!" The great panther leaped as a kitten leaps at a dead leaf whirling overhead, struck left and right into the empty air, that sung under the strokes, landed noiselessly, and leaped again and again, while the half purr, half growl gathered head as steam rumbles in a boiler. "I am Bagheera—in the jungle—in the night, and my strength is in me. Who shall stay my stroke? Man-cub, with one blow of my paw I could beat thy head flat as a dead frog in the summer!"

"Strike, then!" said Mowgli, in the dialect of the village, *not* the talk of the jungle. And the human words brought Bagheera to a full stop, flung back on his haunches that quivered under him, his head just at the level of Mowgli's. Once more Mowgli stared, as he had stared at the rebellious cubs, full into the beryl-green eyes, till the red glare behind their green went out like the light of a lighthouse shut off twenty miles across the sea, till the eyes dropped, and the big head with them—dropped lower and lower, and the red rasp of a tongue grated on Mowgli's instep.

"Brother—Brother—Brother!" the boy whispered, stroking steadily and lightly from the neck along the heaving back. "Be still, be still! It is the fault of the night, and no fault of thine."

"It was the smells of the night," said Bagheera, penitently. "This air cries aloud to me. But how dost *thou* know?"

Of course the air round an Indian village is full of all kinds of smells, and to any creature who does nearly all his thinking through his nose, smells are as maddening as music and drugs are to human beings. Mowgli gentled the panther for a few minutes longer, and he lay down like a cat before a fire, his paws tucked under his breast, and his eyes half shut.

"Thou art of the jungle and *not* of the jungle," he said at last. "And I am only a black panther. But I love thee, Little Brother."

"They are very long at their talk under the tree," Mowgli said, without noticing the last sentence. "Buldeo must have told many tales. They should come soon to drag the woman and her man out of the trap and put them into the Red Flower. They will find that trap sprung. Ho! Ho!"

"Nay, listen," said Bagheera. "The fever is out of my blood now. Let them find *me* there! Few would leave their houses after meeting me. It is not the first time I have been in a cage, and I do not think they will tie *me* with cords."

"Be wise, then," said Mowgli, laughing, for he was beginning to feel as reckless as the panther, who had glided into the hut.

"*Pah!*" Bagheera puffed. "This place is rank with Man, but here is just such a bed as they gave me to lie upon in the king's cages at Oodeypore. Now I lie down." Mowgli heard the strings of the cot crack under the great brute's weight. "By the broken lock that freed me, they will think they have caught big game! Come and sit beside me, Little Brother. We will give them 'good hunting' together!"

"No, I have another thought in my stomach. The man pack shall not know what share I have in the sport. Make thine own hunt. I do not wish to see them."

"Be it so," said Bagheera. "Now they come!"

The conference under the peepul-tree had been growing noisier and noisier, at the far end of the village. It broke in wild yells, and a rush up the street of men and women, waving clubs and bamboos and sickles and knives. Buldeo and the Brahmin were at the head of it, but the mob was close at their heels, and they cried: "The witch and the wizard! Let us see if hot coins will make them confess! Burn the hut over their heads! We will teach them to shelter wolf-devils! Nay, beat them first! Torches! More torches! Buldeo, heat the gun-barrel!"

Here was some little difficulty with the catch of the door. It had been very firmly fastened, but the crowd tore it away bodily, and the light of the torches streamed into the room where, stretched at full length on the bed, his paws crossed and lightly hung down over one end, black as the pit and terrible as a demon, was Bagheera. There was one half-minute of desperate silence, as the front ranks of the crowd clawed and tore their way back from the threshold, and in that minute Bagheera raised his head and yawned—

elaborately, carefully, and ostentatiously—as he would yawn when he wished to insult an equal. The fringed lips drew back and up; the red tongue curled; the lower jaw dropped and dropped till you could see half-way down the hot gullet; and the gigantic dogteeth stood clear to the pit of the gums till they rang together, upper and under, with the snick of steel-faced wards shooting home round the edges of a safe. Next minute the street was empty. Bagheera had leaped back through the window, and stood at Mowgli's side, while a yelling, screaming torrent scrambled and tumbled one over another in their panic haste to get to their huts.

"They will not stir till the day comes," said Bagheera, quietly. "And now?"

The silence of the afternoon sleep seemed to have overtaken the village, but, as they listened, they could hear the sound of heavy grain-boxes being dragged over earthen floors and pushed against doors. Bagheera was quite right. The village would not stir till daylight. Mowgli sat still and thought, and his face grew darker and darker.

"What have I done?" said Bagheera, at last, fawning.

"Nothing but great good. Watch them now till the day. I sleep." Mowgli ran off into the jungle, and dropped across a rock, and slept and slept the day round, and the night back again.

When he waked, Bagheera was at his side, and there lay a newly killed buck at his feet. Bagheera watched curiously while Mowgli went to work with his skinning-knife, ate and drank, and turned over with his chin in his hands.

"The man and the woman came safe within eye-shot of Khanhiwara," Bagheera said. "Thy mother sent the word

241

back by Chil. They found a horse before midnight of the night they were freed, and went very quickly. Is not that well?"

"That is well," said Mowgli.

"And thy man pack in the village did not stir till the sun was high this morning. Then they ate their food and ran back quickly to their houses."

"Did they, by chance, see thee?"

"It may have been. I was rolling in the dust before the gate at dawn, and I may have made also some small song to myself. Now, Little Brother, there is nothing more to do. Come hunting with me and Baloo. He has new hives that he wishes to show, and we all desire thee back again as of old. Take off that look which makes even *me* afraid. The man and woman will not be put into the Red Flower, and all goes well in the jungle. Is it not true? Let us forget the man pack."

"They shall be forgotten—in a little while. Where does Hathi feed to-night?"

"Where he chooses. Who can answer for the Silent One? But why? What is there Hathi can do which we cannot?"

"Bid him and his three sons come here to me."

"But, indeed, and truly, Little Brother, it is not—it is not seemly to say 'Come' and 'Go' to Hathi. Remember, he is the master of the jungle, and before the man pack changed the look on thy face, he taught thee a Master Word of the jungle."

"That is all one. I have a Master Word for him now. Bid him come to Mowgli the Frog, and if he does not hear at first, bid him come because of the sack of the fields of Bhurtpore."

"The sack of the fields of Bhurtpore," Bagheera repeated two or three times to make sure. "I go. Hathi can but be angry at the worst, and I would give a moon's hunting to hear a Master Word that compels the Silent One."

He went away, leaving Mowgli stabbing furiously with his skinning-knife into the earth. Mowgli had never seen human blood in his life before till he had seen, and—what meant much more to him—smelled Messua's blood on the thongs that bound her. And Messua had been kind to him, and, so far as he knew anything about love, he loved Messua as completely as he hated the rest of mankind. But deeply as he loathed them, their talk, their cruelty, and their cowardice, not for anything the jungle had to offer could he bring himself to take a human life, and have that terrible scent of blood back again in his nostrils. His plan was simpler but much more thorough, and he laughed to himself when he thought that it was one of old Buldeo's tales told under the peepul-tree in the evening that had put the idea into his head.

"It *was* a Master Word," Bagheera whispered in his ear. "They were feeding by the river, and they obeyed as though they were bullocks. Look, where they come now!"

Hathi and his three sons had appeared in their usual way, without a sound. The mud of the river was still fresh on their flanks, and Hathi was thoughtfully chewing the green stem of a young plantain-tree that he had gouged up with his tusks. But every line in his vast body showed to

Bagheera, who could see things when he came across them, that it was not the master of the jungle speaking to a man-cub, but one who was afraid coming before one who was not. His three sons rolled side by side, behind their father.

Mowgli hardly lifted his head as Hathi gave him "Good hunting." He kept him swinging and rocking, and shifting from one foot to another, for a long time before he spoke, and when he opened his mouth it was to Bagheera, not to the elephants.

"I will tell a tale that was told to me by the hunter ye hunted to-day," said Mowgli. "It concerns an elephant, old and wise, who fell into a trap, and the sharpened stake in the pit scarred him from a little above his heel to the crest of his shoulder, leaving a white mark." Mowgli threw out his hand, and as Hathi wheeled the moonlight showed a long white scar on his slaty side, as though he had been struck with a red-hot whip. "Men came to take him from the trap," Mowgli continued, "but he broke his ropes, for he was strong, and he went away till his wound was healed. Then came he, angry, by night to the fields of those hunters. And I remember now that he had three sons. These things happened many, many rains ago, and very far away—among the fields of Bhurtpore. What came to those fields at the next reaping, Hathi?"

"They were reaped by me and by my three sons," said Hathi.

"And to the ploughing that follows the reaping?" said Mowgli.

"There was no ploughing," said Hathi.

"And to the men that live by the green crops on the ground?" said Mowgli.

"They went away."

"And to the huts in which the men slept?" said Mowgli.

"We tore the roofs to pieces, and the jungle swallowed up the walls," said Hathi.

"And what more, besides?" said Mowgli.

"As much good ground as I can walk over in two nights from the east to the west, and from the north to the south as much as I can walk over in three nights, the jungle took. We let in the jungle upon five villages, and in those villages, and in their lands, the grazing-ground and the soft crop-grounds, there is not one man to-day who gets his food from the ground. That was the sack of the fields of Bhurtpore, which I and my three sons did. And now I ask, man-cub, how the news of it came to thee?" said Hathi.

"A man told me. And now I see even Buldeo can speak truth. It was well done, Hathi with the white mark, but the second time it shall be done better, for the reason that there is a man to direct. Thou knowest the village of the man pack that cast me out? They are idle, senseless, and cruel; they play with their mouths, and they do not kill their weaker for food, but for sport. When they are full-fed they would throw their own breed into the Red Flower. This I have seen. It is not well that they should live here anymore. I hate them!"

"Kill, then," said the youngest of Hathi's three sons, picking up a tuft of grass, dusting it against his forelegs, and throwing it away, while his little red eyes glanced furtively from side to side.

"What good are white bones to me?" Mowgli answered furiously. "Am I the cub of a wolf to play in the sun with a raw head? I have killed Shere Khan, and his hide rots on the Council Rock, but—but I do not know whither Shere Khan is gone, and my stomach is still empty. Now I will take that which I can see and touch. Let in the jungle upon that village, Hathi!"

Bagheera shivered, and cowered down. He could understand, if the worst came to the worst, a quick rush down the village street, and a right and left blow into a crowd, or a crafty killing of men as they ploughed in the twilight, but this scheme deliberately blotting out an entire village from the eyes of man and beast frightened him. Now he saw why Mowgli had sent for Hathi. No one but the long-lived elephant could plan and carry through such a war.

"Let them run as the men ran from the fields of Bhurtpore, till we have the rain-water for the only plough, and the noise of the rain on the thick leaves for the pattering of their spindles—till Bagheera and I lair in the house of the Brahmin, and the buck drink at the tank behind the temple! Let in the jungle, Hathi!"

"But I—but we have no quarrel with them, and it needs the red rage of great pain ere we tear down the places where men sleep," said Hathi, rocking doubtfully.

"Are ye the only Eaters of Grass in the jungle? Drive in your peoples. Let the deer and the pig and the nilghai look to it. Ye need never show a hand's-breadth of hide till the fields are naked. Let in the jungle, Hathi!"

"There will be no killing? My tusks were red at the sack of the fields of Bhurtpore, and I would not wake that smell again."

"Nor I. I do not wish even their bones to lie on our clean earth. Let them go find a fresh lair. They cannot stay here! I have seen and smelled the blood of the woman that gave me food—the woman whom they would have killed but for me. Only the smell of the new grass on their doorsteps can take away that smell. It burns in my mouth. Let in the jungle, Hathi!"

"Ah!" said Hathi. "So did the scar of the stake burn on my hide till we watched the villages die under in the spring growth. Now I see. Thy war shall be our war. We will let in the jungle."

Mowgli had hardly time to catch his breath—he was shaking all over with rage and hate—before the place where the elephants had stood was empty, and Bagheera was looking at him with terror.

"By the broken lock that freed me!" said the black panther at last. "Art *thou* the naked thing I spoke for in the pack when all was young? Master of the jungle, when my strength goes, speak for me—speak for Baloo—speak for us all! We are cubs before thee! Snapped twigs under foot! Fawns that have lost their doe!"

The idea of Bagheera being a stray fawn upset Mowgli altogether, and he laughed and caught his breath, and sobbed and laughed again, till he had to jump into a pool to make himself stop. Then he swam round and round, ducking in and out of the bars of the moonlight like the frog, his namesake.

By this time Hathi and his three sons had turned, each to one point of the compass, and were striding silently down the valleys a mile away. They went on and on for two days' march—that is to say, a long sixty miles—through the jungle, while every step they took, and every wave of their trunks, was known and noted and talked over by Mang and Chil and the Monkey-People and all the birds. Then they began to feed, and fed quietly for a week or so. Hathi and his sons are like Kaa the Rock Python. They never hurry till they have to.

At the end of that time—and none knew who had started it—a rumour went through the jungle that there was better food and water to be found in such and such a valley. The pigs—who, of course, will go to the ends of the earth for a full meal—moved first by companies, scuffling over the rocks, and the deer followed, with the little wild foxes that live on the dead and dying of the herds; and the heavy-shouldered nilghai moved parallel with the deer, and the wild buffaloes of the swamps came after the nilghai. The least little thing would have turned the scattered, straggling droves that grazed and sauntered and drank and grazed again, but whenever there was an alarm someone would rise up and soothe them. At one time it would be Sahi the Porcupine, full of news of good feed just a little farther on; at another Mang would cry cheerily and flap down a glade to show it was all empty; or Baloo, his mouth full of roots, would shamble alongside a wavering line and half frighten, half romp it clumsily back to the proper road. Very many creatures broke back or ran away or lost interest, but very many were left to go forward. At the end of another ten days or so the situation was this. The deer and the pig and the nilghai were milling round and round in a circle of eight or ten miles' radius, while the Eaters of Flesh skirmished round its edge. And the centre of that circle was the village, and round the village the crops were ripening, and in the crops sat men on what they call *machans*— platforms like pigeon-perches, made of sticks at the top of four poles—to scare away birds and other stealers. Then the deer were coaxed no more. The Eaters of Flesh were close behind them, and forced them forward and inward.

It was a dark night when Hathi and his three sons slipped down from the jungle, and broke off the poles of the *machans* with their trunks, and they fell as a snapped stalk of hemlock in bloom falls, and the men that tumbled from them heard the deep gurgling of the elephants in their ears. Then the vanguard of the bewildered armies of the deer broke down and flooded into the village grazing-grounds and the ploughed fields; and the sharp-hoofed, rooting wild pig came with them, and what the deer left the pig spoiled, and from time to time an alarm of wolves would shake the herds, and they would rush to and fro desperately, treading down the young barley, and cutting flat the banks of the irrigating channels. Before the dawn broke the pressure on the outside of the circle gave way at one point. The Eaters of Flesh had fallen back and left an open path to the south, and drove upon drove of buck fled along it. Others, who were bolder, lay up in the thickets to finish their meal next night.

But the work was practically done. When the villagers looked in the morning they saw their crops were lost. That meant death if they did not get away, for they lived year in and year out as near to starvation as the jungle was near to them. When the buffaloes were sent to graze the hungry brutes found that the deer had cleared the grazing-grounds, and so wandered into the jungle and drifted off with their wild mates; and when twilight fell the three or four ponies that belonged to the village lay in their stables with their heads beaten in. Only Bagheera could have given those strokes, and only Bagheera could have thought of insolently dragging the last carcass to the open street.

The villagers had no heart to make fires in the fields that night, so Hathi and his three sons went gleaning among what was left, and where Hathi gleans there is no need to follow. The men decided to live on their stored seed-corn until the rains had fallen, and then to take work as servants till they could catch up with the lost year. But as the grain-dealer was thinking of his well-filled crates of corn, and the prices he would levy at the sale of it, Hathi's sharp tusks were picking out the corner of his mud-house, and smashing up the big wicker-chest, leeped with cow-dung, where the precious stuff lay.

When that last loss was discovered, it was the Brahmin's turn to speak. He had prayed to his own gods without answer. It might be, he said, that, unconsciously, the village had offended some one of the gods of the jungle, for, beyond doubt, the jungle was against them. So they sent for the head-man of the nearest tribes of wandering Gonds—little, wise, and very black hunters, living in the deep jungle, whose fathers came of the oldest race in India—the aboriginal owners of the land. They made the

Gond welcome with what they had, and he stood on one leg, his bow in his hand, and two or three poisoned arrows stuck through his top-knot, looking half afraid and half contemptuously at the anxious villagers and their ruined fields. They wished to know whether his gods—the Old Gods—were angry with them, and what sacrifices should be offered. The Gond said nothing, but picked up a trail of the *karela,* the vine that bears the bitter wild gourd, and laced it to and fro across the temple door in the face of the staring red Hindu image. Then he pushed with his hand in the open air along the road to Khanhiwara, and went back to his jungle, and watched the Jungle-People drifting through it. He knew that when the jungle moves only white men can hope to turn it aside.

There was no need to ask his meaning. The wild gourd would grow where they had worshipped their god, and the sooner they saved themselves the better.

But it is hard to tear a village from its moorings. They stayed on as long as any summer food was left to them, and they tried to gather nuts in the jungle, but shadows with glaring eyes watched them, and rolled before them even at mid-day, and when they ran back afraid to their walls, on the tree-trunks they had passed not five minutes before the bark would be striped and chiselled with the stroke of some great taloned paw. The more they kept to their village, the bolder grew the wild things that gambolled and bellowed on the grazing-grounds by the Wainganga. They had no heart to patch and plaster the rear walls of the empty byres that backed on to the jungle; the wild pig trampled them down, and the knotty-rooted vines hurried after and threw their elbows over the new-won ground, and the coarse grass bristled behind the vines. The unmarried men ran away first, and carried the news far and near that the village was doomed. Who could fight, they said, against the jungle, or the gods of the jungle, when the very village cobra had left his hole in the platform under the peepul? So their little commerce with the outside world shrank as the trodden paths across the open grew fewer and fainter. And the nightly trumpetings of Hathi and his three sons ceased to trouble them; they had no more to go. The crop on the ground and the seed in the ground had been taken. The outlying fields were already losing their shape, and it was time to throw themselves on the charity of the English at Khanhiwara.

Native fashion, they delayed their departure from one day to another till the first rains caught them and the unmended roofs let in a flood, and the grazing-ground stood ankle deep, and all green things came on with a rush after the heat of the summer. Then they waded out—men, women, and children—through the blinding hot rain of the morning, but turned naturally for one farewell look at their homes.

They heard, as the last burdened family filed through the gate, a crash of falling beams and thatch behind the walls. They saw a shiny, snaky black trunk lifted for an instant, scattering sodden thatch. It disappeared, and there was another crash, followed by a squeal. Hathi had been plucking off the roofs of the huts as you pluck water-lilies, and a rebounding beam had pricked him. He needed only this to unchain his full strength, for of all things in the jungle the wild elephant enraged is the most wantonly destructive. He kicked backwards at a mud wall that crumbled at the stroke, and, crumbling, melted to yellow mud under the torrents of rain. Then he wheeled and squealed, and tore through the narrow streets, leaning against the huts right and left, shivering the crazy doors, and crumpling up the eaves, while his three sons raged behind as they had raged at the sack of the fields of Bhurtpore.

"The jungle will swallow these shells," said a quiet voice in the wreckage. "It is the outer walls that must lie down." And Mowgli, with the rain sluicing over his bare shoulders and arms, leaped back from a wall that was settling like a tired buffalo.

"All in good time," panted Hathi. "Oh, but my tusks were red at Bhurtpore! To the outer wall, children! With the head! Together! Now!"

The four pushed side by side. The outer wall bulged, split, and fell, and the villagers, dumb with horror, saw the savage, clay-streaked heads of the wreckers in the ragged gap. Then they fled, houseless and foodless, down the valley, as their village, shredded and tossed and trampled, melted behind them.

A month later the place was a dimpled mound, covered with soft, green young stuff, and by the end of the rains there was the roaring jungle in full blast on the spot that had been under plough not six months before.

I will let loose against you the fleet-footed vines—
I will call in the jungle to stamp out your lines!
 The roofs shall fade before it,
  The house-beams shall fall,
 And the *karela,* the bitter *karela,*
  Shall cover it all!

In the gates of these your councils my people shall sing,
In the doors of these your garners the Bat-Folk shall cling;
 And the snake shall be your watchman,
  By a hearthstone unswept;
 For the *karela,* the bitter *karela,*
  Shall fruit where ye slept!

Ye shall not see my strikers; ye shall hear them and guess;
By night, before the moon-rise, I will send for my cess,
 And the wolf shall be your herdsman
  By a landmark removed,
 For the *karela,* the bitter *karela,*
  Shall seed where ye loved!

I will reap your fields before you at the hands of a host;
Ye shall glean behind my reapers for the bread that is lost;
   And the deer shall be your oxen
     By a headland untilled,
   For the *karela,* the bitter *karela,*
     Shall leaf where ye build!

I have untied against you the club-footed vines,
I have sent in the jungle to swamp out your lines.
   The trees—the trees are on you!
    The house-beams shall fall,
   And the *karela,* the bitter *karela,*
     Shall cover you all!

THE SPRING RUNNING

Rudyard Kipling

The second year after the great fight with Red Dog and the death of Akela,* Mowgli must have been nearly seventeen years old. He looked older, for hard exercise, the best of good eating, and baths whenever he felt in the least hot or dusty had given him strength and growth far beyond his age. He could swing by one hand from a top branch for half an hour at a time, when he had occasion to look along the tree-roads. He could stop a young buck in mid-gallop and throw him sideways by the head. He could even jerk over the big blue wild boars that lived in the Marshes of the North. The Jungle-People, who used to fear him for his wits, feared him now for his mere strength, and when he

---

* The story "Red Dog" tells how Mowgli leads the victorious
  fight against a huge pack of rampaging dholes who threaten the
  Seeonee wolves. In the battle, Akela is killed.

moved quietly on his own affairs the whisper of his coming cleared the wood-path. And yet the look in his eyes was always gentle. Even when he fought his eyes never glazed as Bagheera's did. They only grew more and more interested and excited, and that was one of the things that Bagheera himself did not understand.

He asked Mowgli about it, and the boy laughed and said: "When I miss the kill I am angry. When I go empty for two days I am very angry. Do not my eyes talk then?"

"The mouth is hungry," said Bagheera, "but the eyes say nothing. Hunting, eating, or swimming, it is all one—like a stone in wet or dry weather." Mowgli looked at him lazily from under his long eyelashes, and, as usual, the panther's head dropped. Bagheera knew his master.

They were lying out far up the side of a hill overlooking the Wainganga, and the morning mists lay below them in bands of white and green. As the sun rose they changed into bubbling seas of red and gold, churned off and let the low rays stripe the dried grass on which Mowgli and Bagheera were resting. It was the end of the cold weather, the leaves and the trees looked worn and faded, and there was a dry ticking rustle when the wind blew. A little leaf tap-tap-tapped furiously against a twig as a single leaf caught in a current will. It roused Bagheera, for he snuffed the morning air with a deep hollow cough, threw himself on his back, and struck with his forepaws at the nodding leaf above.

"The year turns," he said. "The jungle goes forward. The Time of New Talk is near. That leaf knows. It is very good."

"The grass is dry," Mowgli answered, pulling up a tuft. "Even Eye-of-the-Spring [that is a little, trumpet-shaped, waxy red flower that runs in and out among the grasses]— even Eye-of-the-Spring is shut and . . . Bagheera, *is* it well for the Black Panther so to lie on his back and beat with his paws in the air as though he were the tree-cat?"

"Aowh!" said Bagheera. He seemed to be thinking of other things.

"I say, *is* it well for the Black Panther so to mouth and cough and howl and roll? Remember, we be the masters of the jungle, thou and I."

"Indeed, yes. I hear, man-cub." Bagheera rolled over hurriedly, and sat up, the dust on his ragged black flanks. (He was just casting his winter coat.) "We be surely the masters of the jungle! Who is so strong as Mowgli? Who so wise?" There was a curious drawl in the voice that made Mowgli turn to see whether by any chance the black panther were making fun of him, for the jungle is full of words that sound like one thing but mean another. "I said we be beyond question the masters of the jungle," Bagheera repeated. "Have I done wrong? I did not know that the man-cub no longer lay upon the ground. Does he fly, then?"

Mowgli sat with his elbows on his knees looking out across the valley at the daylight. Somewhere down in the woods below a bird was trying over in a husky, reedy voice the first few notes of his spring song. It was no more than a shadow of the full-throated tumbling call he would be crying later, but Bagheera heard it.

"I said the Time of New Talk was near," growled the panther, switching his tail.

"I hear," Mowgli answered. "Bagheera, why dost thou shake all over? The sun is warm."

"That is Ferao, the scarlet woodpecker," said Bagheera. "*He* has not forgotten. Now I too must remember my song." And he began purring and crooning to himself, harking back dissatisfied again and again.

"There is no game afoot," said Mowgli, lazily.

"Little Brother, are *both* thine ears stopped? That is no killing-word but my song that I make ready against the need."

"I had forgotten. I shall know when the Time of New Talk is here, because then thou and the others run away and leave me single-foot." Mowgli spoke rather savagely.

"But, indeed, Little Brother," Bagheera began, "we do not always—"

"I say ye do," said Mowgli, shooting out his forefinger angrily. "Ye *do* run away, and I, who am the master of the jungle, must needs walk single-foot. How was it last season, when I would gather sugar-cane from the fields of a man pack? I sent a runner—I sent thee!—to Hathi bidding him to come upon such a night and pluck the sweet grass for me with his trunk."

"He came only two nights later," said Bagheera, cowering a little, "and of that long sweet grass that pleased thee so, he gathered more than any man-cub could eat in all the nights of the rains. His was no fault of mine."

"He did not come upon the night when I sent him the word. No, he was trumpeting and running and roaring through valleys in the moonlight. His trail was like the trail of three elephants, for he would not hide among the trees.

He danced in the moonlight before the houses of the man pack. I saw him, and yet he would not come to me; and *I* am the master of the jungle!"

"It was the Time of New Talk," said the panther, always very humble. "Perhaps, Little Brother, thou didst not that time call him by a Master Word? Listen to Ferao!"

Mowgli's bad temper seemed to have boiled itself away. He lay back with his head on his arms, his eyes shut. "I do not know—nor do I care," he said sleepily. "Let us sleep, Bagheera. My stomach is heavy in me. Make me a rest for my head."

The panther lay down again with a sigh, because he could hear Ferao practising and repractising his song against the Spring-time of New Talk, as they say.

In an Indian jungle the seasons slide one into the other almost without division. There seem to be only two—the wet and the dry—but if you look closely below the torrents of rain and the clouds of char and dust you will find all four going round in their regular order. Spring is the most wonderful, because she has not to cover a clean bare field with new leaves and flowers, but to drive before her and to put away the hanging-on, over-surviving raffle of half-green things which the gentle winter has suffered to live, and to make the partly dressed, stale earth feel new and young once more. And this she does so well that there is no spring in the world like the jungle spring.

There is one day when all things are tired, and the very smells as they drift on the heavy air are old and used. One cannot explain, but it feels so. Then there is another day— to the eye nothing whatever has changed—when all the smells are new and delightful and the whiskers of the Jungle-People quiver to their roots, and the winter hair comes away from their sides in long draggled locks. Then, perhaps, a little rain falls, and all the trees and the bushes and the bamboos and the mosses and the juicy-leaved plants wake with a noise of growing that you can almost hear, and under this noise runs, day and night, a deep hum. *That* is the noise of the spring—a vibrating boom which is neither bees nor falling water nor the wind in the tree-tops, but the purring of the warm, happy world.

Up to this year Mowgli had always delighted in the turn of the seasons. It was he who generally saw the first Eye-of-the-Spring deep down among the grasses, and the first bank of spring clouds which are like nothing else in the jungle. His voice could be heard in all sorts of wet star-lighted blossoming places, helping the big frogs through their choruses, or mocking the little upside-down owls that hoot through the white nights. Like all his people, spring was the season he chose for his flittings—moving for mere joy of rushing through the warm air, thirty, forty, or fifty miles between twilight and the morning star, and coming back panting and laughing and wreathed with strange flowers. The Four did not follow him on these wild ringings of the jungle, but went off to sing songs with other wolves. The Jungle-People are very busy in the spring, and Mowgli could hear them grunting and screaming and whistling according to their kind. Their voices then are different from their voices at other times of the year, and that is one of the reasons why spring is called the Time of New Talk.

But that spring, as he told Bagheera, his stomach was new in him. Ever since the bamboo shoots turned spotty-brown he had been looking forward to the morning when the smells should change. But when that morning came, and Mor the Peacock, blazing in bronze and blue and gold, cried it aloud all along the misty woods, and Mowgli opened his mouth to send on the cry, the words choked between his teeth, and a feeling came over him that began at his toes and ended in his hair—a feeling of pure unhappiness—and he looked himself over to be sure that he had not trodden on a thorn. Mor cried the new smells, the other birds took it over, and from the rocks by the Wainganga he heard Bagheera's hoarse scream—something between the scream of an eagle and the neighing of a horse. There was a yelling and scattering of *Bandar-log* in the new-budding branches above, and there stood Mowgli, his chest filled to answer Mor, sinking in little gasps as the breath was driven out of it by this unhappiness.

He stared, but he could see no more than the mocking *Bandar-log* scudding through the trees, and Mor, his tail spread in full splendour, dancing on the slopes below.

"The smells have changed," screamed Mor. "Good hunting, Little Brother! Where is thy answer?"

"Little Brother, good hunting!" whistled Chil the Kite and his mate swooping down together. The two baffed under Mowgli's nose so close that a pinch of downy white feathers brushed out.

A light spring rain—elephant-rain they call it—drove across the jungle in a belt half a mile wide, left the new leaves wet and nodding behind, and died out in a double rainbow and a light roll of thunder. The spring-hum broke out for a minute and was silent, but all the Jungle-Folk seemed to be giving tongue at once. All except Mowgli.

"I have eaten good food," he said to himself. "I have drunk good water. Nor does my throat burn and grow small, as it did when I bit the blue-spotted root that Oo the Turtle said was clean food. But my stomach is heavy, and I have, for no cause, given very bad talk to Bagheera and others, people of the jungle and my people. Now, too, I am hot and now I am cold, and now I am neither hot nor cold, but angry with that which I cannot see. *Huhu!* It is time to make a running! To-night I will cross the ranges; yes, I will make a spring running to the Marshes of the North and back again. I have hunted too easily too long. The Four shall come with me, for they grow as fat as white grubs."

He called, but never one of the Four answered. They were far beyond earshot, singing over the spring songs—the moon and sambur songs—with the wolves of the pack, for in the spring-time the Jungle-People make little difference between the day and the night. He gave the sharp barking note, but his only answer was the mocking *maiou* of the little spotted tree-cat winding in and out among the branches for early birds' nests. At this he shook all over with rage and half drew his knife. Then he became very haughty, though there was no one to see him, and stalked severely down the hillside, chin up and eyebrows down. But never a single one of his people asked him a question, for they were all too busy with their own affairs.

"Yes," said Mowgli to himself, though in his heart he knew that he had no reason. "Let the red dhole come from the Dekkan or the Red Flower dance among the bamboos, and all the jungle runs whining to Mowgli calling him great elephant names. But now, because Eye-of-the-Spring is red, and Mor, forsooth, must show his naked legs in some spring-dance, the jungle goes mad as Tabaqui. . . . By the bull that bought me, am I the master of the jungle or am I not? Be silent! What do ye here?"

A couple of young wolves of the pack were cantering down a path looking for open ground in which to fight. (You will remember that the Law of the Jungle forbids fighting where the pack can see.) Their neck-bristles were as stiff as wire, and they bayed, furiously crouching for the first grapple. Mowgli leaped forward, caught one outstretched throat in either hand, expecting to fling the creatures backwards, as he had often done in games or pack hunts. But he had never before interfered with a spring fight. The two leaped forward and dashed him aside to the earth, and without a word to waste rolled over and over close locked.

Mowgli was on his feet almost before he fell, his knife and his white teeth were bared, and at that minute he would have killed both for no reason but that they were fighting when he wished them to be quiet, although every wolf has full right under the Law to fight. He danced round them with lowered shoulders and quivering hand ready to send in a double blow when the first flurry of the scuffle should be over, but while he waited the strength seemed to go out of his body, the knife point lowered, and he sheathed the knife and watched.

"I have eaten poison," he said at last. "Since I broke up the council with the Red Flower—since I killed Shere Khan none of the pack would fling me aside. And these be only tail-wolves in the pack, little hunters. My strength is gone from me, and presently I shall die. O, Mowgli, why dost thou not kill them both?"

The fight went on till one wolf ran away, and Mowgli was left alone on the torn and bloody ground, looking now at his knife, and now at his legs and arms, while the feeling of unhappiness he had never known before covered him as water covers a log.

He killed early that evening and ate but little, so as to be in good fettle for his spring running, and he ate alone because all the Jungle-People were away singing or fighting. It was a perfect white night, as they call it. All green things seemed to have made a month's growth since the morning. The branch that was yellow-leaved the day before dripped sap when Mowgli broke it. The mosses curled deep and warm over his feet, the young grass had no cutting edges, and all the voices of the jungle boomed like one deep harp-string touched by the moon—the full Moon of New Talk, who splashed her light full on rock and pool, slipped it between trunk and creeper, and sifted it through the million leaves. Unhappy as he was, Mowgli sang aloud with pure delight as he settled into his stride. It was more like flying than anything else, for he had chosen the long downward slope that leads to the northern marshes through the heart of the main jungle, where the springy ground deadened the fall of his feet. A man-taught man would have picked his way with many stumbles through the cheating moonlight, but Mowgli's muscles, trained by years of experience, bore him up as though he were a feather. When a rotten log or a hidden stone turned under his foot he saved himself, never checking his pace, without effort and without thought. When he tired of ground-going he threw up his hands monkey-fashion to the nearest creeper, and seemed to float rather than to climb up into the thin branches, whence he would follow a tree-road till his mood changed, and he shot downwards in a long leafy curve to the levels again. There were still hot hollows surrounded by wet rocks where he could hardly breathe for the heavy scents of the night-flowers, and the bloom along the creeper-buds; dark avenues where the moonlight lay in belts as regular as chequered marbles in a church aisle; thickets where the wet young growth stood breast-high about him and threw its arms round his waist; and hilltops crowned with broken rock, where he leaped from stone to stone above the lairs of the frightened little foxes. He would hear, very faint and far off, the *chug-drug* of a boar sharpening his tusks on a bole; and later would come across the great brute all alone, scribing and rending the red bark of a tree, his mouth dripping with foam and his eyes blazing like fire. Or he would turn aside to the sound of clashing horns and hissing grunts and dash past a couple of furious sambur, staggering to and fro with lowered heads, striped with blood that shows black in the moonlight. Or at some rushing ford he would hear Jacala the Crocodile bellowing like a bull, or disturb a knot of the Poison-People, but before they could strike he would be away and across the glistening shingle, and deep into the jungle again.

So he ran, sometimes shouting, sometimes singing to himself, the happiest thing in all the jungle that night, till the smell of the flowers warned him that he was near the marshes, and those lay far beyond his farthest hunting-grounds.

Here, again, a man-trained man would have sunk over his head in three strides, but Mowgli's feet had eyes in them and they passed him from tussock to tussock and clump to quaking clump without asking help from the eyes in his head. He headed out to the middle of the swamp, disturbing the duck as he ran, and sat down on a moss-coated tree-trunk lapped in the black water. The marsh was awake all round him, for in the spring the Bird-People sleep very lightly, and companies of them were coming or going the night through. But no one took any notice of Mowgli sitting among the tall reeds humming songs without words and looking at the soles of his hard brown feet in case of neglected thorns. All his unhappiness seemed to have been left behind in his own jungle, and he was just beginning a song when it came back again—ten times worse than before. To make all worse the moon was setting.

This time Mowgli was frightened. "It is here also!" he said half aloud. "It has followed me," and he looked over his shoulder to see whether the It were not standing behind him. "There is no one here." The night noises in the marsh went on, but never bird or beast spoke to him, and the new feeling of misery grew.

"I have eaten poison," he said, in an awe-stricken voice. "It must be that carelessly I have eaten poison, and my strength is going from me. I was afraid—and yet it was not *I* that was afraid—Mowgli was afraid when the two wolves fought. Akela, or even Phao, would have silenced them, yet Mowgli was afraid. That is sure sign I have eaten poison. . . . But what do they care in the jungle? They sing and howl and fight, and run in companies under the moon, and I— *Hai mai!*—I am dying in the marshes, of that poison which I have eaten." He was so sorry for himself that he nearly wept. "And after," he went on, "they will find me lying in the black water. Nay, I will go back to my own jungle and I will die upon the Council Rock, and Bagheera whom I love, if he is not screaming in the valley, Bagheera, perhaps, may watch by what is left for a little, lest Chil use me as he used Akela."

A large warm tear splashed down on his knee, and, miserable as he was, Mowgli felt happy that he was so miserable, if you can understand that upside-down sort of happiness. "As Chil the Kite used Akela," he repeated, "on the night I saved the pack from Red Dog." He was quiet for a little, thinking of the last words of the Lone Wolf,* which you, of course, remember. "Now Akela said to me many foolish things before he died, for when we die our stomachs change. He said . . . None the less, I *am* of the jungle!"

---

* Mortally wounded in a fight against Red Dog, Akela tells Mowgli, "Thou art a man, Little Brother," and entreats him to "Go to thine own people."

In his excitement, as he remembered the fight on Wainganga bank, he shouted the last words aloud, and a wild buffalo-cow among the reeds sprang to her knees, snorting: "Man!"

"*Uhh!*" said Mysa the Wild Buffalo (Mowgli could hear him turn in his wallow), "*that* is no man. It is only the hairless wolf of the Seeonee Pack. On such nights runs he to and fro."

"*Uhh!*" said the cow, dropping her head again to graze, "I thought it was Man."

"I say no. Oh, Mowgli, is it danger?" lowed Mysa.

"Oh, Mowgli, is it danger?" the boy called back mockingly. "That is all Mysa thinks for: Is it danger? But for Mowgli, who goes to and fro in the jungle by night watching, what care ye?"

"How loud he cries?" said the cow.

"Thus do they cry," Mysa answered contemptuously, "who having torn the grass up know not how to eat it."

"For less than this," Mowgli groaned to himself, "for less than this even last rains I had pricked Mysa out of his wallow and ridden him through the swamp on a rush halter." He stretched his hand to break one of the feathery reeds, but drew it back with a sigh. Mysa went on steadily chewing the cud and the long grass ripped where the cow grazed. "I will not die *here*," he said angrily. "Mysa, who is of one blood with Jacala and the pig, would mock me. Let us go beyond the swamp, and see what comes. Never have I run such a spring running—hot and cold together. Up, Mowgli!"

He could not resist the temptation of stealing across the reeds to Mysa and pricking him with the point of his knife. The great dripping bull broke out of his wallow like a shell exploding, while Mowgli laughed till he sat down.

"Say now that the hairless wolf of the Seeonee Pack once herded thee, Mysa," he called.

"Wolf! *Thou*?" the bull snorted, stamping in the mud. "All the jungle knows thou wast a herder of tame cattle— such a man's brat as shouts in the dust by the crops yonder. *Thou* of the jungle! What hunter would have crawled like a snake among the leeches, and for a muddy jest—a jackal's jest—have shamed me before my cow? Come to firm ground, and I will—I will . . ." Mysa frothed at the mouth, for he has nearly the worst temper of anyone in the jungle.

Mowgli watched him puff and blow with eyes that never changed. When he could make himself heard through the spattering mud-shower, he said: "What man pack lair here by the marshes, Mysa? This is new jungle to me."

"Go north, then," roared the angry bull, for Mowgli had pricked him rather sharply. "It was a naked cowherd's jest. Go and tell them at the village at the foot of the marsh."

"The man pack do not love jungle-tales, nor do I think, Mysa, that a scratch more or less on thy hide is any matter for a council. But I will go and look at this village. Yes, I will go. Softly now! It is not every night that the master of the jungle comes to herd thee."

He stepped out to the shivering ground on the edge of the marsh, well knowing that Mysa would never charge over it, and laughed, as he ran, to think of the bull's anger.

"My strength is not altogether gone," he said. "It may be the poison is not to the bone. There is a star sitting low yonder." He looked at it steadily between half-shut hands. "By the bull that bought me, it is the Red Flower—the Red Flower that I lay beside before—before I came even to the first Seeonee Pack! Now that I have seen I will finish the running."

The marsh ended in a broad plain where a light twinkled. It was a long time since Mowgli had concerned himself with the doings of men, but this night the glimmer of the Red Flower drew him forward as if it had been new game.

"I will look," said he, "and I will see how far the man pack has changed."

Forgetting that he was no longer in his own jungle where he could do what he pleased, he trod carelessly through the dew-loaded grasses till he came to the hut where the light stood. Three or four yelping dogs gave tongue, for he was on the outskirts of a village.

"Ho!" said Mowgli, sitting down noiselessly, after sending back a deep wolf-growl that silenced the curs. "What comes will come. Mowgli, what hast thou to do anymore with the lairs of the man pack?" He rubbed his mouth, remembering where a stone had struck it years ago when the other man pack had cast him out.

The door of the hut opened and a woman stood peering out into the darkness. A child cried, and the woman said over her shoulder: "Sleep. It was but a jackal that waked the dogs. In a little time morning comes."

Mowgli in the grass began to shake as though he had the fever. He knew that voice well, but to make sure he cried softly, surprised to find how man's talk came back: "Messua! O Messua!"

"Who calls?" said the woman, a quiver in her voice.

"Hast thou forgotten?" said Mowgli. His throat was dry as he spoke.

"If it be *thou,* what name did I give thee? Say!" She had half shut the door, and her hand was clutching at her breast.

"Nathoo! Ohé Nathoo!" said Mowgli, for, as you know, that was the name Messua gave him when he first came to the man pack.

"Come, my son," she called, and Mowgli stepped into the light, and looked full at Messua, the woman who had been good to him, and whose life he had saved from the man pack so long before. She was older, and her hair was grey, but her eyes and her voice had not changed. Woman-like, she expected to find Mowgli where she had left him, and her eyes travelled upwards in a puzzled fashion from his chest to his head, that touched the top of the door.

"My son," she stammered, and then sinking to his feet: "But it is no longer my son. It is a godling of the woods! *Ahai!*"

As he stood in the red light of the oil-lamp, strong, tall, and beautiful, his long black hair sweeping over his shoulders, the knife swinging at his neck, and his head crowned with a wreath of white jasmine, he might easily have been mistaken for some wild god of a jungle legend. The child half asleep on a cot sprang up and shrieked aloud with terror. Messua turned to soothe him while Mowgli stood still, looking in at the water-jars and cooking-pots, the grain-bin and all the other human belongings that he found himself remembering so well.

"What wilt thou eat or drink?" Messua murmured. "This is all thine. We owe our lives to thee. But art thou him I called Nathoo, or a godling, indeed?"

"I am Nathoo," said Mowgli. "I am very far from my own place. I saw this light and came hither. I did not know thou wast here."

"After we came to Khanhiwara," Messua said timidly, "the English would have helped us against those villagers that sought to burn us. Rememberest thou?"

"Indeed, I have not forgotten."

"But when the English Law was made ready we went to the village of those evil people and it was no more to be found."

"That also I remember," said Mowgli, with a quiver of the nostril.

"My man, therefore, took service in the fields, and at last, for indeed he was a strong man, we held a little land here. It is not so rich as the old village, but we do not need much—we two."

"Where is he—the man that dug in the dirt when he was afraid on that night?"

"He is dead—a year."

"And he?" Mowgli pointed to the child.

"My son that was born two rains ago. If thou art a godling give him the favour of the jungle that he may be safe among thy—thy people as we were safe on that night."

She lifted up the child, who, forgetting his fright, reached out to play with the knife that hung on Mowgli's chest, and Mowgli put the little fingers aside very carefully.

"And if thou art Nathoo whom the tigers carried away," Messua went on choking, "he is then thy younger brother. Give him an elder brother's blessing."

"Hai mai! What do I know of the thing called a blessing? I am neither a godling nor his brother, and—O Mother, Mother, my heart is heavy in me." He shivered as he set down the child.

"Like enough," said Messua, bustling among the cooking-pots. "This comes of running about the marshes by night. Beyond question, a fever has soaked thee to the marrow." Mowgli smiled a little at the idea of anything in the jungle hurting him. "I will make a fire and thou shalt drink warm milk. Put away the jasmine wreath, the smell is heavy in so small a place."

Mowgli sat down, muttering, his face in his hands. All manner of strange feelings were running over him, exactly as though he had been poisoned, and he felt dizzy and a little sick. He drank the warm milk in long gulps, Messua patting him on the shoulder from time to time, not quite sure whether he were her son Nathoo of the long-ago days or some wonderful jungle being, but glad to feel that he was at least flesh and blood.

"Son," she said at last. Her eyes were full of pride. "Have any told thee that thou art beautiful beyond all men?"

"Hah?" said Mowgli, for of course he had never heard anything of the kind. Messua laughed softly and happily. The look in his face was enough for her.

"I am the first, then? It is right, though it comes seldom, that a mother should tell her son these good things. Thou art very beautiful. Never have I looked upon such a man."

Mowgli twisted his head and tried to see over his own hard shoulder, and Messua laughed again so long that Mowgli, not knowing why, was forced to laugh with her, and the child ran from one to the other laughing too.

"Nay, thou must not mock thy brother," said Messua, catching him to her breast. "When thou art one-half as fair we will marry thee to the youngest daughter of a king and thou shalt ride great elephants."

Mowgli could not understand one word in three of the talk here; the warm milk was taking effect on him after his forty-mile run; so he curled up and in a minute was deep asleep, and Messua put the hair back from his eyes, threw a cloth over him and was happy. Jungle-fashion, he slept out the rest of that night and all the next day, for his instincts, which never wholly slept, warned him there was nothing to fear. He waked at last with a bound that shook the hut, for the cloth over his face made him dream of traps, and there he stood, his hand on his knife, the sleep all heavy in his rolling eyes, ready for any fight.

Messua laughed and set the evening meal before him. There were only a few coarse cakes baked over the smoky fire, some rice, and a lump of sour preserved tamarinds— just enough to go on with till he could get to his evening kill. The smell of the dew in the marshes made him hungry and restless. He wanted to finish his spring running, but the child insisted on sitting in his arms, and Messua would have it that his long blue-black hair must be combed out.

So she sang as she combed, foolish little baby songs, now calling Mowgli her son, and now begging him to give some of his jungle-power to the child. The hut door was closed, but Mowgli heard a sound he knew well, and saw Messua's jaw drop with horror as a great grey paw came under the bottom of the door, and Grey Brother outside whined a muffled and penitent whine of anxiety and fear.

"Out and wait. Ye would not come when I called," said Mowgli in jungle-talk, never turning his head, and the great grey paw disappeared.

"Do not—do not bring thy—thy servants with thee," said Messua. "I—we have always lived at peace with the jungle."

"It is peace," said Mowgli, rising. "Think of that night on the road to Khanhiwara. There were scores of such folk before thee and behind thee. But I see that even in springtime the Jungle-People do not always forget. Mother, I go."

Messua drew aside humbly—he was indeed a wood-god she thought—but as his hand was on the door the mother in her made her throw her arms round Mowgli's neck again and again.

"Come back!" she whispered. "Son or no son, come back, for I love thee—and look, he too grieves."

The child was crying because the man with the shiny knife was going away.

"Come back again," Messua repeated. "By night or by day this door is never shut to thee."

Mowgli's throat worked as though the cords in it were being pulled, and his voice seemed to be dragged from it as he answered: "I will surely come back."

"And now," he said, as he put aside the head of the fawning wolf on the threshold, "I have a little cry against thee, Grey Brother. Why came ye not, all Four, when I called so long ago?"

"So long ago? It was but last night. I—we—were singing in the jungle, the new songs, for this is the Time of New Talk. Rememberest thou?"

"Truly, truly."

"And as soon as the songs were sung," Grey Brother went on earnestly, "I followed thy trail. I ran from all the others and followed hot-foot. But, O Little Brother, what hast *thou* done—eating and sleeping with the man pack?"

"If ye had come when I called this had never been," said Mowgli, running much faster.

"And now what is to be?" said Grey Brother.

Mowgli was going to answer when a girl in a white cloth came down some path that led from the outskirts of the village. Grey Brother dropped out of sight at once and Mowgli backed noiselessly into a field of high-springing crops. He could almost have touched her with his hand when the warm green stalks closed before his face and he disappeared like a ghost. The girl screamed, for she thought she had seen a spirit, and then she gave a deep sigh. Mowgli parted the stalks with his hands and watched her till she was out of sight.

"And now I do not know," he said, sighing in his turn. "*Why* did ye not come when I called?"

"We follow thee—we follow thee," Grey Brother mumbled, licking at Mowgli's heel. "We follow thee always except in the Time of the New Talk."

"And would ye follow me to the man pack?" Mowgli whispered.

"Did I not follow thee on the night that our old pack cast thee out? Who waked thee lying among the crops?"

"Aye, but again?"

"Have I not followed thee to-night?"

"Aye, but again and again, and it may be again, Grey Brother?"

Grey Brother was silent. When he spoke he growled to himself: "The Black One spoke truth."

"And he said?"

"Man goes to Man at the last. Raksha our mother said—"

"So also said Akela on the night of Red Dog," Mowgli muttered.

"So also said Kaa, who is wiser than us all."

"What dost thou say, Grey Brother?"

"They cast thee out once, with bad talk. They cut thy mouth with stones. They sent Buldeo to slay thee. They would have thrown thee into the Red Flower. Thou, and not I, hast said that they are evil and senseless. Thou and not I—I follow my own people—didst let in the jungle upon them. Thou and not I didst make song against them more bitter even than our song against Red Dog."

"I ask thee what *thou* sayest?"

They were talking as they ran. Grey Brother cantered on a while without replying, and then he said between bound and bound as it were: "Man-cub—master of the jungle—son of Raksha—lair-brother to me—though I forget for a little while in the spring, thy trail is my trail, thy lair is my lair, thy kill is my kill, and thy death-fight is my death-fight."

I speak for the Three. But what wilt thou say to the jungle?"

"That is well thought. Between the sight and the kill it is not good to wait. Go before and cry them all to the Council Rock, and I will tell them what is in my stomach. But they may not come—in the Time of the New Talk they may forget me."

"Hast thou then forgotten nothing?" snapped Grey Brother over his shoulder, as he laid himself down to gallop, and Mowgli followed, thinking.

At any other season his news would have called all the jungle together with bristling necks, but now they were busy hunting and fighting and killing and singing. From one to another Grey Brother ran, crying: "The master of the jungle goes back to Man. Come to the Council Rock!" And the happy, eager people only answered: "He will return in the summer heats. The rains will drive him to lair. Run and sing with us, Grey Brother."

"But the master of the jungle goes back to Man," Grey Brother would repeat.

"*Eee—Yowa?* Is the Time of New Talk any less good for that?" they would reply. So when Mowgli, heavyhearted, came up through the well-remembered rocks to the place where he had been brought into the pack, he found only the Four, Baloo, who was nearly blind with age, and the heavy, cold-blooded Kaa, coiled round Akela's empty seat.

"Thy trail ends here, then, manling?" said Kaa, as Mowgli threw himself down, his face in his hands. "Cry thy cry. We be of one blood, thou and I—man and snake together."

"Why was I not torn in two by Red Dog?" the boy moaned. "My strength is gone from me, and it is not the poison. By night and by day I hear a double step upon my trail. When I turn my head it is as though one had hidden himself from me that instant. I go to look behind the trees and he is not there. I call and none cry again, but it is as though one listened and kept back the answer. I lie down, but I do not rest. I run the spring running, but I am not made still. I bathe, but I am not made cool. The kill sickens me, but I have no heart to fight except I kill. The Red Flower is in my body, my bones are water—and—I know not what I know."

"What need of talk?" said Baloo, slowly, turning his head to where Mowgli lay. "Akela by the river said it, that Mowgli should drive Mowgli back to the man pack. I said it. But who listens now to Baloo? Bagheera—where is Bagheera this night? He knows also. It is the Law."

"When we met at the Cold Lairs, manling, I knew it," said Kaa, turning a little in his mighty coils. "Man goes to Man at the last, though the jungle does not cast him out."

The Four looked at one another and at Mowgli, puzzled but obedient.

"The jungle does not cast me out, then?" Mowgli stammered.

Grey Brother and the Three growled furiously, beginning: "So long as we live none shall dare—" But Baloo checked them.

"I taught thee the Law. It is for me to speak," he said, "and though I cannot now see the rocks before me, I see far. Little frog, take thine own trail; make thy lair with thine own blood and pack and people; but when there is need of foot or tooth or eye or a word carried swiftly by night, remember, master of the jungle, the jungle is thine at call."

"The Middle Jungle is thine also," said Kaa. "I speak for no small people."

"*Hai mai,* my brothers," cried Mowgli, throwing up his arms with a sob. "I know not what I know, I would not go, but I am drawn by both feet. How shall I leave these nights?"

"Nay, look up, Little Brother," Baloo repeated. "There is no shame in this hunting. When the honey is eaten we leave the empty hive."

"Having cast the skin," said Kaa, "we may not creep into it afresh. It is the Law."

"Listen, dearest of all to me," said Baloo. "There is neither word nor will here to hold thee back. Look up! Who may question the master of the jungle? I saw thee playing among the white pebbles yonder when thou wast a little frog; and Bagheera, that bought thee for the price of a young bull newly killed, saw thee also. Of that looking-over we two only remain, for Raksha, thy lair-mother, is dead with thy lair-father; the old wolf pack is long since dead; thou knowest whither Shere Khan went, and Akela died among the dholes, where but for thy wisdom and strength the second Seeonee Pack would also have died. There remain nothing but old bones. It is no longer the man-cub that asks leave of his pack, but the master of the jungle that changes his trail. Who shall question man in his ways?"

"But Bagheera and the bull that bought me," said Mowgli. "I would not—"

His words were cut short by a roar and a crash in the thicket below, and Bagheera, light, strong, and terrible as always.

"Therefore," he said, stretching out a dripping right paw, "I did not come. It was a long hunt, but he lies dead in the bushes now—a bull in his second year—the bull that frees thee, Little Brother. All debts are paid now. For the rest, my word is Baloo's word." He licked Mowgli's foot. "Remember Bagheera loved thee," he cried and bounded away. At the foot of the hill he cried again long and loud: "Good hunting on a new trail, master of the jungle! Remember Bagheera loved thee."

"Thou hast heard," said Baloo. "There is no more. Go now, but first come to me. O wise little frog, come to me!"

"It is hard to cast the skin," said Kaa, as Mowgli sobbed and sobbed with his head on the blind bear's side and his arms round his neck, while Baloo tried feebly to lick his feet.

"The stars are thin," said Grey Brother, snuffing at the dawn-wind. "Where shall we lair to-day? For, from now, we follow new trails."

And this is the last of the Mowgli stories.

THE OUTSONG

This Is the Song That Mowgli Heard Behind Him in the Jungle Till He Came to Messua's Door Again.

BALOO

For the sake of him who showed
One wise frog the jungle-road,
Keep the Law the man pack make—
For thy blind old Baloo's sake!
Clean or tainted, hot or stale,
Hold it as it were the trail,
Through the day and through the night,
Questing neither left nor right.
For the sake of him who loves
Thee beyond all else that moves,
When thy pack would make thee pain,
Say: "Tabaqui sings again."
When thy pack would work thee ill,
Say: "Shere Khan is yet to kill."
When the knife is drawn to slay,
Keep the Law and go thy way.
(Root and honey, palm and spathe,
Guard a cub from harm and scathe.)
Wood and water, wind and tree,
Jungle-favour go with thee!

KAA

Anger is the egg of fear—
Only lidless eyes are clear.
Cobra-poison none may leech;
Even so with cobra-speech.
Open talk shall call to thee
Strength whose mate is courtesy.
Send no lunge beyond thy length;
Lend no rotten bough thy strength.
Gauge thy gape with buck or goat,
Lest thine eye should choke thy throat.
After gorging, wouldst thou sleep?
Look thy den is hid and deep,
Lest a wrong, by thee forgot,
Draw thy killer to the spot.
East and West and North and South,
Wash thy skin and close thy mouth.
(Pit and rift and blue pool-brim
Middle Jungle follow him!)
Wood and water, wind and tree,
Jungle-favour go with thee!

BAGHEERA

In the cage my life began;
Well I know the ways of Man.
By the broken lock that freed—
Man-cub 'ware the man-cub's breed!
Scenting-dew or starlight pale,
Choose no idle tree-cat trail.
Pack or council, hunt or den,
Cry no truce with Jackal-Men.
Feed them silence when they say:
"Come with us an easy way."
Feed them silence when they seek
Help of thine to hurt the weak.
Make no *bandar's* boast of skill;
Hold thy peace above the kill.
Let not call nor song nor sign
Turn thee from thy hunting-line.
(Morning mist or twilight clear
Serve him, wardens of the deer!)
Wood and water, wind and tree,
Jungle-favour go with thee!

THE THREE

On the trail that thou must tread
To the threshold of our dread,
Where the flower blossoms red;
Through the nights when thou shalt lie
Prisoned from our mother-sky,
Hearing us, thy loves, go by;
In the dawns, when thou shalt wake
To the toil thou canst not break,
Heartsick for the jungle's sake;
Wood and water, wind and tree,
Jungle-favour go with thee!

ACKNOWLEDGMENTS

All possible care has been taken to trace ownership and secure permission for
each selection in this series. The Great Books Foundation wishes to thank
the following authors, publishers, and representatives for permission to reprint
copyrighted material:

The Veldt, by Ray Bradbury. Copyright 1950 by Ray Bradbury; renewed 1977
by Ray Bradbury. Reprinted by permission of Don Congdon Associates, Inc.

The White Umbrella, by Gish Jen, first published in THE YALE REVIEW, 1984.
Copyright 1984 by Gish Jen. Reprinted by permission of the author.

The Parsley Garden, from THE ASSYRIAN AND OTHER STORIES,
by William Saroyan. Copyright 1949 by William Saroyan. Reprinted by
permission of the William Saroyan Foundation.

As the Night the Day, by Abioseh Nicol, from MODERN AFRICAN PROSE,
edited by Richard Rive. Copyright 1964 by Abioseh Nicol. Reprinted by
permission of Harold Ober Associates, Inc.

Playing Venice, The Cat, and *The Robe,* from THE SUMMER BOOK,
by Tove Jansson, translated by Thomas Teal. Translation copyright 1975
by Random House, Inc. Reprinted by permission of Pantheon Books,
a division of Random House, Inc.

The Alligators, from THE SAME DOOR, by John Updike. Copyright 1958
by John Updike. First published in *The New Yorker.* Reprinted by permission
of Alfred A. Knopf, Inc.

The Magic Jacket, from COLLECTED STORIES FOR CHILDREN,
by Walter de la Mare. Copyright 1947 by the Estate of Walter de la Mare.
Reprinted by permission of The Literary Trustees of Walter de la Mare
and The Society of Authors as their representative.

Props for Faith, from FLOATING IN MY MOTHER'S PALM, by Ursula Hegi.
Copyright 1990 by Ursula Hegi. Reprinted by permission of Poseidon Books,
a division of Simon & Schuster, Inc.

ILLUSTRATION CREDITS